FIRESIDE TALES
FROM
PEMBROKESHIRE

VOLUME THREE OF THE FOLK TALES TRILOGY
Brian John

GREENCROFT BOOKS
Newport, Pembrokeshire, SA42 OQN

Printed in Wales

GREENCROFT BOOKS

FIRESIDE TALES FROM PEMBROKESHIRE
VOLUME THREE OF THE FOLK TALES TRILOGY

First Edition 1993

Published by Greencroft Books, Trefelin, Cilgwyn, Newport,
Pembs SA42 OQN. Tel: 0239-820470

DEDICATION

To the memory of my mother Gwladys John, who died on October 13th, 1992. She enjoyed a good story and a good laugh, and encouraged me to do the same. And to those who have kindly sent me stories, some new and some old, for inclusion in this third volume of the Folk Tales Trilogy.

Designed by Brian John

Printed in Wales from publisher's typesetting by C.I.T. Printing Services Ltd of Haverfordwest.

Cover illustration from a painting by Graham Hadlow

The story illustrations come from the following nineteenth-century annuals: *The Boy's Own Paper, The Girl's Own Paper, Sunday, Gleanings from Popular Authors Grave and Gay*, and *Harper's Young People*.

ISBN 0 905559 67 3

CONTENTS

..... *Rhiannon, as beautiful as ever, entered the hall in the company of her father.* (See p 28)

PREFACE

This is the third volume of the Pembrokeshire Folk Tales Trilogy. It follows the publication of **Pembrokeshire Folk Tales** in 1991 and **The Last Dragon** in 1992. Since commencing work on the series in 1990 I have been inundated with tales from Pembrokeshire people, including many from exiles now living far away. They acknowledge that they are prompted by a sense of *Hiraeth* to record their memories and the stories which they were told as children. I thank them and all the other Pembrokeshire people who have kindly taken an interest in my folk tale project. Sadly, I have not been able to use all the tales submitted to me, and I apologise to any readers whose material does not find its way into print. With this volume the total number of tales published in the series reaches 338, and difficult editorial choices have to be made with respect to story length, balance between sections and so forth. I still have more than 50 splendid unpublished tales on file.........

As with the previous volumes, I hope that the stories contained in this little book will appeal to readers as varied, informative and entertaining. Important sources have been **Folk-Lore of Mid and West Wales** (1911) by J. Ceredig Davies, **The Antiquities of Laugharne, Pendine and their Neighbourhoods** (1880) by Mary Curtis, and the writings of local authors including Dillwyn Miles, Roscoe Howells, Francis Jones, and Roger Worsley.

However, undoubtedly the richest source of material for this book has been a hand-written manuscript by the Rev W. Meredith Morris, completed around 1899 and clearly intended by its author for publication. It is entitled **The Folklore of South Pembrokeshire**, and its 100 or so pages are a veritable treasure-house of wonderful stories collected mostly around 1890-99 from all parts of Pembrokeshire.

In the pages which follow I have made no attempt to analyse the stories or to look for original sources or connections between them. Again, I leave that task to those who make a special study of folklore; but to help those who want to research certain stories which might be of interest to them, I have again given full details as to my sources. For those with a geographical turn of mind I have also included in this volume four maps which show the places of residence of all the Pembrokeshire fairies, witches, magicians, phantoms and ghosts featured in **The Folk Tales Trilogy**. So far as I know, these are the first such maps ever published!

As usual, it is a pleasure to thank all those who have helped in the creation of this book, and in particular Mary John and her colleagues at the Haverfordwest Public Library; Graham Hadlow for the cover illustration; Roscoe Howells for the dust-jacket photograph; Sally Rudman for assistance with typesetting; Rod Crow, Neil Davies and their colleagues at CIT Printing Services for their efficiency and expertise in the printing process. Finally I must thank my wife Inger for her constant support and help in listening to the stories, advising on wording, proofreading and many other matters.

INTRODUCTION

The title of this book awakens memories of a cold winters night and a crackling fire in the living-room grate. There is a smoking oil lamp on the mantelpiece. Father is settled into his favourite armchair, with a cat on his lap. He has an old book in his hand, and he is reading from it, in measured tones, to a little group of avid listeners. The children sit on the rug before the fire, their upturned and rosy faces illuminated by the flickering light of the flames. They have had their supper, and they have just climbed out of a steaming hot bath. The smell of carbolic soap lingers about them. There is time for just one more story before bed-time ....

This simple and even banal picture may not mean much to modern children or their parents, who take central heating, electric light, television and radio for granted. It may be difficult for them to appreciate how important the fireside was at the heart of the home, or to imagine the intimacy and security provided by the storytelling ritual on the hearth-rug. However, for those born during or before the Second World War the image of "fireside tales" will be strong and full of meaning, and it has been my intention in putting together this little book to awaken the memories of those old enough to have experienced culm balls in the fireplace and to have read **The Boy's Own Paper**. At the same time, I want to fire the imaginations of the young and to remind them that there is more to life than violent video games and synthetic TV heroes. Indeed, many of the children of today do not realise that there is a wealth of wonderful stories accociated with places which they know and with names which they can read on the gravestones in the local churchyard.

Following the warm reception given to the first two volumes of The Folk Tales Trilogy, I have decided to keep to the well-tried formula used in **Pembrokeshire Folk Tales** and **The Last Dragon**. All of the tales used in this book are new; and as before they have been culled from a great variety of sources. For those who wish to study the tales I have provided full citations, and I have mentioned individuals by name where they have provided unique stories. There is a glossary of Welsh terms, a comprehensive bibliography, and a listing of story locations.

The maps on pages 10 - 13 are an innovation. Having now collected almost 350 Pembrokeshore folk tales, and having been forced by my background to look at them in a geographical light, it seemed entirely natural that the distribution of Pembrokeshire fairies, corpse candles, ghosts, witches and other strange phenomena should be properly mapped. So far as I know, nobody has ever mapped these things before. In particular, I hope that the maps will prove helpful to visitors as they drive around the county looking for churches, castles and cromlechs; now they can also look for dragons, hounds of hell, and phantom funerals. Maybe we should press the County Council for some proper signposting!

As in the previous volumes, the book is divided into eight sections. We begin with a section entitled **Tales of the Saints** (6 tales), followed by a section on **Heroic Deeds** (8 tales), and a section on **Strange Happenings** (21 tales).Then follows a group of 11 **Fairy Tales** and a section on **Witchcraft and Magic** (18 tales). Next comes a section of 15 strange tales on **Signs, Omens and Portents**, and a group of 16 favourite **Ghostly Tales**. In the final section of the book there are 15 tales of **Folk Heroes, Great and Small** which are difficult to classify elsewhere. One innovation in the present collection is the inclusion of a number of tales of charms and charmers, both of which figure very prominently in local folk traditions.

While working on this current collection I have been impressed once again by the frailty of mankind and by the obvious morality of the tales. One is reinforced in one's belief that the tales have been used over the centuries in order to teach children (and adults!) how to behave and to strengthen the civilised values of Pembrokeshire society. As we have seen before, dishonesty, avarice, and deceit are always punished, whereas virtue is always rewarded. Only occasionally are the lines of demarcation blurred; what is one to make, for example, of tales 3.15 and 3.18?

One difference between this book and the previous two volumes is the emphasis I have been able to give to some of the lesser-known tales buried away in the Pembrokeshire literature. In addition to wildly eccentric folk heroes such as Shemi Wad of Goodwick, Twm Waunbwll of Glandwr, Twm Carnabwth of Mynachlog-ddu, and Wil Canaan, we can now add Gwilym ap Owen, George Owen, Mary Palmer, Old Moll of Redberth, and Bill Frost. Many of the stories in Sections 3 and 8 have, so far as I know, never before been published in a readily accessible form; and it has been a pleasure to dig them out and dust them down.

At this point I should like to emphasise the debt which students of Pembrokeshire folk-lore owe to the Rev W. Meredith Morris. Mention has already been made in the Preface of the "lost" manuscript of his book entitled **The Folklore of South Pembrokeshire**. I still recall with pleasure the sheer excitement of looking through this manuscript for the first time. Most of the reverend gentleman's tales are about fairies, witchcraft and sorcery, ghosts, premonitions and omens, but there is also much valuable material on local superstitions, old customs, and charms. The manuscript itself is housed at the Central Library in Cardiff, but it is available to students of folk-lore on microfilm at the Haverfordwest County Library.

Meredith Morris was born in 1867 and brought up in the Gwaun Valley in North Pembrokeshire, where it was perhaps inevitable that he should encounter various tales of the supernatural; as a young man he recorded several of these tales. He was probably a member of Jabez Chapel at Pontfaen. In 1892, at the age of 25, he moved to become a Baptist minister in Cresswell Quay in South Pembrokeshire; and from then until his move to the Vale of Glamorgan in 1899 he collected many more strange tales particularly from the Pembroke-Narberth area. Most of these tales have never before appeared in print, and it is a pleasure to bring 27 of them to the attention of a much wider readership in this new volume.

Brian John
October 1993

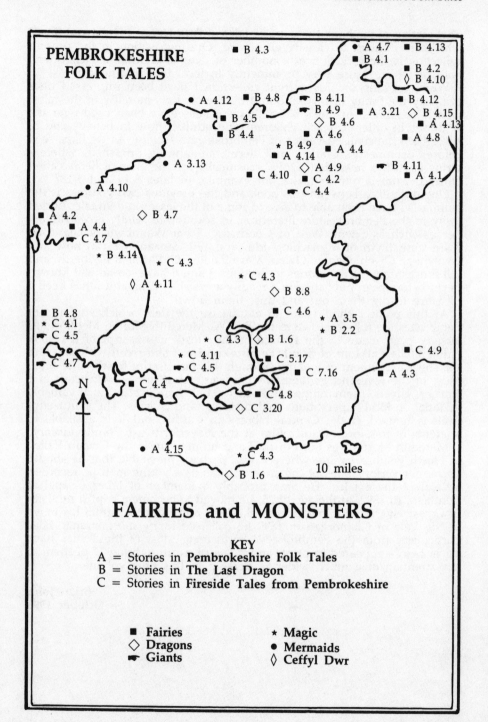

PEMBROKESHIRE
FOLK TALES

■ B 4.3   ● A 4.7   ■ B 4.13
             ■ B 4.1
                         ■ B 4.2
                         ◇ B 4.10

■ A 4.12   ■ B 4.8   ☛ B 4.11   ■ B 4.12
           ■ B 4.5   ■ B 4.9   A 3.21   ◇ B 4.15
           ■ B 4.4   ◇ B 4.6   ■ A 4.13
                      ■ A 4.6   ■ A 4.8
              ★ B 4.9   ■ A 4.4
              ■ A 4.14
● A 3.13   ■ C 4.10 ◇ A 4.9   ☛ B 4.11
                        ■ C 4.2   ■ A 4.1
● A 4.10   ☛ C 4.4

■ A 4.2   ◇ B 4.7
■ A 4.4
☛ C 4.7
      ★ B 4.14   ★ C 4.3
         ◊ A 4.11   ★ C 4.3
                       ◇ B 8.8
■ B 4.8   ■ C 4.6
★ C 4.1   ★ A 3.5
☛ C 4.5   ★ B 2.2
         ★ C 4.3   ◇ B 1.6   ■ C 4.9
      ★ C 4.11   ■ C 5.17
      ☛ C 4.5   ■ C 7.16   ■ A 4.3
■ C 4.4
         ■ C 4.8
         ◇ C 3.20

N

● A 4.15   ★ C 4.3
                              10 miles
         ◇ B 1.6

FAIRIES and MONSTERS

KEY

A = Stories in **Pembrokeshire Folk Tales**
B = Stories in **The Last Dragon**
C = Stories in **Fireside Tales from Pembrokeshire**

■ **Fairies**   ★ **Magic**
◇ **Dragons**   ● **Mermaids**
☛ **Giants**   ◊ **Ceffyl Dwr**

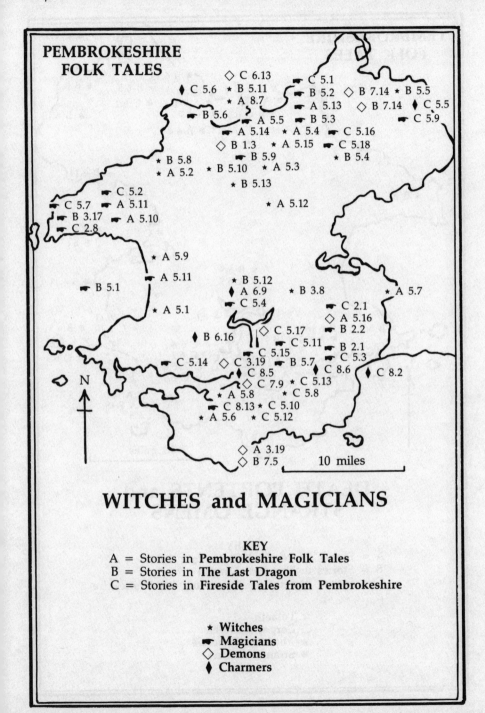

PEMBROKESHIRE
FOLK TALES

◇ C 6.13
★ B 5.11   ◼ C 5.1
♦ C 5.6   ◼ B 5.2   ◇ B 7.14 ★ B 5.5
★ A 8.7   ◼ A 5.13   ◇ B 7.14 ♦ C 5.5
◼ B 5.6   ◼ A 5.5   ◼ B 5.3   ◼ C 5.9
A 5.14   ★ A 5.4   ◼ C 5.16
◇ B 1.3   ★ A 5.15   ◼ C 5.18
◼ B 5.9   ★ B 5.4
★ B 5.8   ◼ B 5.10   ★ A 5.3
★ A 5.2
★ B 5.13

◼ C 5.2
C 5.7   ◼ A 5.11   ★ A 5.12
◼ B 3.17   ◼ A 5.10
C 2.8

★ A 5.9

◼ B 5.1   ◼ A 5.11   ★ B 5.12
♦ A 6.9   ★ B 3.8   ★ A 5.7
★ A 5.1   ◼ C 5.4   ◼ C 2.1
                          ◇ A 5.16
♦ B 6.16   ◼ B 2.2
           ◇ C 5.17
           ◼ C 5.11   ◼ B 2.1
           C 5.15   ◼ C 5.3
◼ C 5.14   ◇ C 3.19 ◼ B 5.7   ◼ C 8.6   ♦ C 8.2
           ♦ C 8.5
           ◇ C 7.9 ★ C 5.13
           ★ A 5.8 ★ C 5.8
           ◼ C 8.13 ★ C 5.10
           ★ A 5.6 ★ C 5.12

           ◇ A 3.19
           ◇ B 7.5   10 miles

N

WITCHES and MAGICIANS

KEY
A = Stories in **Pembrokeshire Folk Tales**
B = Stories in **The Last Dragon**
C = Stories in **Fireside Tales from Pembrokeshire**

★ **Witches**
◼ **Magicians**
◇ **Demons**
♦ **Charmers**

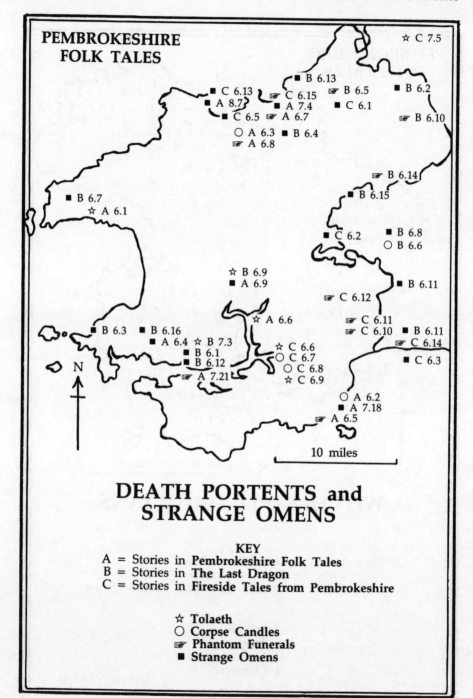

**PEMBROKESHIRE
FOLK TALES**

☆ C 7.5

■ B 6.13

■ C 6.13   ☞ C 6.15   ☞ B 6.5   ■ B 6.2
■ A 8.7   ■ A 7.4   ■ C 6.1
  ■ C 6.5   ☞ A 6.7   ☞ B 6.10
      ○ A 6.3   ■ B 6.4
      ☞ A 6.8

                                    ☞ B 6.14
                              ■ B 6.15

■ B 6.7   ■ C 6.2   ■ B 6.8
☆ A 6.1   ○ B 6.6

                ☆ B 6.9
                ■ A 6.9   ☞ C 6.12   ■ B 6.11

                              ☆ A 6.6   ☞ C 6.11
                                          ☞ C 6.10   ■ B 6.11
■ B 6.3   ■ B 6.16   ☞ C 6.14
      ■ A 6.4 ☆ B 7.3   ☆ C 6.6   ■ C 6.3
          B 6.1   ○ C 6.7
N   B 6.12   ○ C 6.8
        ☞ A 7.21   ☆ C 6.9

                          ○ A 6.2
                          ■ A 7.18
                    ☞ A 6.5

                    10 miles

DEATH PORTENTS and
STRANGE OMENS

KEY
A = Stories in **Pembrokeshire Folk Tales**
B = Stories in **The Last Dragon**
C = Stories in **Fireside Tales from Pembrokeshire**

☆ **Tolaeth**
○ **Corpse Candles**
☞ **Phantom Funerals**
■ **Strange Omens**

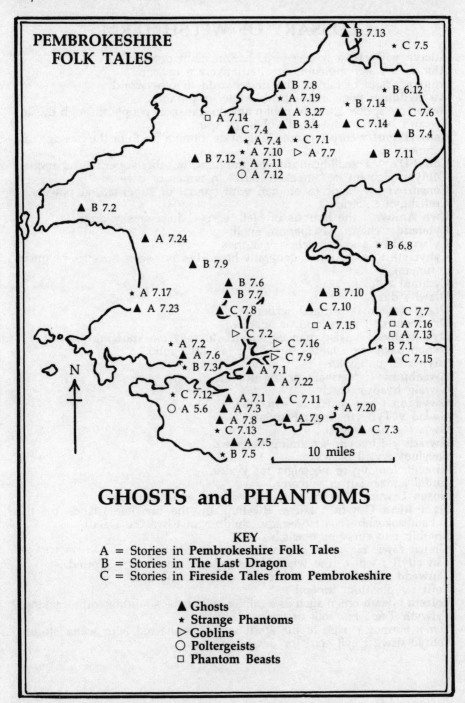

PEMBROKESHIRE
FOLK TALES

□ A 7.14
▲ C 7.4
★ A 7.4
★ A 7.10
★ A 7.11
○ A 7.12
▲ B 7.12

▲ B 7.8
★ A 7.19
▲ A 3.27
▲ B 3.4
★ C 7.1
▷ A 7.7

▲ B 7.13
★ C 7.5
★ B 6.12
★ B 7.14
▲ C 7.6
▲ C 7.14
▲ B 7.4
▲ B 7.11

▲ B 7.2

▲ A 7.24

▲ B 7.9

★ B 6.8

▲ B 7.6
▲ B 7.7
◁ C 7.8

▲ B 7.10
▲ C 7.10
□ A 7.15

▲ C 7.7
□ A 7.16
□ A 7.13

★ A 7.17
▲ A 7.23

▷ C 7.2
▷ C 7.16
▷ C 7.9

★ B 7.1
▲ C 7.15

★ A 7.2
▲ A 7.6
★ B 7.3
▲ A 7.1
▲ A 7.22
★ C 7.12
○ A 5.6
▲ A 7.1
▲ A 7.3
▲ A 7.8
★ C 7.13
▲ A 7.5
★ B 7.5

▲ C 7.11
▲ A 7.9

★ A 7.20
▲ C 7.3

N

10 miles

GHOSTS and PHANTOMS

KEY
A = Stories in **Pembrokeshire Folk Tales**
B = Stories in **The Last Dragon**
C = Stories in **Fireside Tales from Pembrokeshire**

▲ Ghosts
★ Strange Phantoms
▷ Goblins
○ Poltergeists
□ Phantom Beasts

GLOSSARY OF WELSH TERMS

Aderyn y Gorff: a corpse bird, harbinger of death.
Afanc : a water monster, or alternatively a beaver.
Annwn : land of fairies, the underworld or otherworld.
Awenyddion: poets who speak while in a trance.
Bwbach: a sprite, ghost or goblin able to transport people through the air.
Bwca: a helpful household goblin or spirit.
Canwyll gorff : corpse candle, a light denoting a death or the passage of a funeral.
Ceffyl Dwr : a small beautiful spectral horse or other supernatural animal.
Coblyn: a goblin, a "knocker spirit" in mines or caves.
Consuriwr : a magician or man with special or supernatural powers.
Crefishgyn : spirit.
Cwn Annwn : the hounds of Hell, corpse dogs or sky dogs.
Cyfaredd : charm, fascination, spell.
Cyfarwydd : a skilled teller of stories.
Cyhyraeth : death omen, generally heard but not seen; spectre; phantom funeral.
Cythraul : devil.
Diawl : devil.
Draig: dragon or winged serpent.
Drychiolaeth : apparition or spectre.
Dyn hysbys : a wise man or wizard (literally : a knowing one).
Dynon bach teg : fairies (literally : fair little folk).
Ellyll : elf or goblin.
Gwenhudwy : mermaid or sea divinity.
Gwraig hyspys: witch.
Gwyddon : hag, witch or sorceress.
Gwlad y Tylwyth Teg : Fairyland
Gwrach : hag, witch.
Gwrach y Rhybyn: screaming banshee.
Gwylnos : vigil or wake.
Hiraeth: longing or nostalgia for Wales.
Hudol : magician or sorcerer.
Noson Lawen : "merry evening" of light entertainment.
Plant Rhys Ddwfn : fairies dwelling on the invisible islands off the Pembrokeshire coast (literally: children of Rhys the Deep).
Rheibio : to curse or bewitch.
Simnai fawr: big open fireplace or inglenook.
Tân ellyll : will o' the wisp, dancing light over boggy ground.
Tanwedd : death omen in the form of a falling light.
Toili : a phantom funeral.
Tolaeth : death omen such as a tolling bell or the sound of coffin-making.
Tylwyth Teg : fair folk or fairies.
Ychen bannog : oxen of the spirit world, connected with water stories.
Ysbryd drwg : evil spirit or devil.

THE SOURCES OF THE STORIES

BENNETT, T. 1982 **Welsh Shipwrecks, Vol 2**, Laidlaw-Burgess, Haverfordwest, 63 pp.

BRINTON, P. & WORSLEY, R. 1987 **Open Secrets**, Gomer, Llandysul, 196 pp.

BROMWICH, R. 1961 **Trioedd Ynys Prydain (The Welsh Triads)**, Univ of Wales Press, Cardiff, 555 pp.

CURTIS, M. 1880 **The Antiquities of Laugharne, Pendine, and their Neighbourhoods**, republished 1991, Dyfed CC, Carmarthen, 339 pp.

DAVIES, J.C. 1911 **Folk-lore of Mid and West Wales**, Welsh Gazette, Aberystwyth, 341 pp.

EVANS WENTZ, W.Y. 1911 **The Fairy-Faith of the Celtic Countries** (Reprint 1981), Humanities Press, Bucks, 524 pp.

FENTON, R. 1811 **A Historical Tour through Pembrokeshire**, London, 388 pp.

GALE, J. 1992 **The Maenclochog Railway**, Milford Haven, 75 pp.

GEOFFREY OF MONMOUTH, 1150 **The History of the Kings of England** (trans. Lewis Thorpe 1966), Penguin, 373 pp.

GIRALDUS CAMBRENSIS, 1188 **The Journey through Wales** (trans. Lewis Thorpe 1978), Penguin, 333 pp.

GODDARD, T. 1983 **Pembrokeshire Shipwrecks**, Hughes, Swansea, 198 pp.

GWYNDAF, R. 1977 - 1990 **Welsh Folk Museum Tapes** (recordings transcribed in Welsh and English).

GWYNDAF, R. **Shemi Wad**, Welsh Folk Museum (typescript), 11 pp.

HALL, S.C. and A.M. 1861 **The Book of South Wales**, reprinted 1977 by EP Publishing, Wakefield, 512 pp.

HOWELLS, R. 1968 **The Sounds Between**, Gomer, Llandysul, 192 pp.

HOWELLS, R. 1977 **Old Saundersfoot**, Gomer, Llandysul, 133 pp.

HOWELLS, R. 1984 **Caldey**, Gomer, Llandysul, 261 pp.

HOWELLS, W. 1831 **Cambrian Superstitions**, Longman, London, 194 pp.

JAMES, D.G. 1957 **The Town and County of Haverfordwest**, J.W. Hammond, Haverfordwest, 172 pp.

JAMES, D.W. 1981 **St David's and Dewisland**, Univ of Wales Press, Cardiff, 228 pp.

JOHN, B.S. 1979 **Honey Harfat: a Haverfordwest Miscellany**, Greencroft Books, Newport, 65 pp.

JONES, E. 1978 **Folk Tales of Wales**, Gomer, Llandysul, 135 pp.

JONES, F. 1953 "Family Tales from Dyfed", **Trans. Hon. Soc. Cymm.**, p 61.

JONES, G. and JONES, T. 1976 **The Mabinogion**, Dent, London, 273 pp.

JONES, T.G. 1930 **Welsh Folk-Lore and Folk Custom** (Reprint 1979), Brewer, Cambridge, 255 pp.

LAWS, E. 1888 **The History of Little England Beyond Wales**, Bell, London, 458 pp.

LOCKLEY, R.M. 1943 **Dream Island Days**, Witherby, London, 144 pp.

MILES, D. 1983 **A Pembrokeshire Anthology**, Hughes, Llandybie, 269 pp.

MILES, D. 1984 **Portrait of Pembrokeshire**, Hale, London 223 pp.

MOLLOY, P. 1983 **And they blessed Rebecca**, Gomer, Llandysul, 352 pp.

MORRIS, B.L. 1948 **The Slebech Story**, Haverfordwest, 81 pp.

PARRY-JONES, D. 1988 **Welsh Legends and Fairy Lore**, Batsford, London, 181 pp.
PHILLIPS, W.D. 1926 **Old Haverfordwest**, J.W. Hammond, Haverfordwest, 121 pp.
PUGH, J. 1986 **Welsh Ghosts and Phantoms**, Emeralda, Cardiff, 112 pp.
PUGH, J. 1987 **Welsh Witches and Warlocks**, Gwasg Carreg Gwalch, Llanrwst, 120 pp.
REES, J.Rogers 1897 "Pembrokeshire Fairies", **Wales** IV, pp 15 - 17.
REES, J. Rogers 1897 "Skomar Oddy", **Wales** IV, pp 68-70.
REES, N. 1992 **St David of Dewisland**, Gomer, Llandysul, 37 pp.
REES, W.J. 1853 **Lives of the Cambro-British Saints**, Welsh MSS Society, Llandovery, 636 pp.
RHYS, J. 1901 **Celtic Folklore : Welsh and Manx** (2 Vols), Oxford, 717 pp.
RICHARDS, W.L. 1992 **Changing Face of Haverfordwest**, Civic Society, Haverfordwest, 150 pp.
ROBERTS, A. 1974 **Myths and Legends of Pembrokeshire**, Abercastle, 32 pp.
SIKES, W. 1880 **British Goblins** (Reprint 1973), E.P. Publishing, Wakefield, 412 pp.
SPENCER, R. 1991 **A Guide to the Saints of Wales and the West Country**, Llanerch, Lampeter, 112 pp.
THOMAS, W.G. 1992 **Llangwm Essays and Sketches**, Elidaprint, Haverfordwest, 64 pp.
THOMAS, W.J. 1952 **The Welsh Fairy Book**, Univ. of Wales Press, Cardiff.
TIMMINS, Thornhill 1895 **Nooks and Corners of Pembrokeshire**, Elliot Stock, London, 197 pp.
TREVELYAN, M. 1909 **Folk-Lore and Folk-Stories of Wales**, Stock, London, 350 pp.
VAUGHAN, H.M. 1926 **The South Wales Squires**, Methuen, London, 216 pp.
WILLIAMS, D. 1955 **The Rebecca Riots**, Univ. of Wales Press, Cardiff, 377 pp.
WILLIAMS, J. 1971 **Give Me Yesterday**, Gwasg Gomer, Llandysul, 154 pp.
WORSLEY, R. 1988 **The Pembrokeshire Explorer**, Coastal Cottages of Pembrokeshire, Abercastle, 127 pp.

THE STORY LOCATIONS

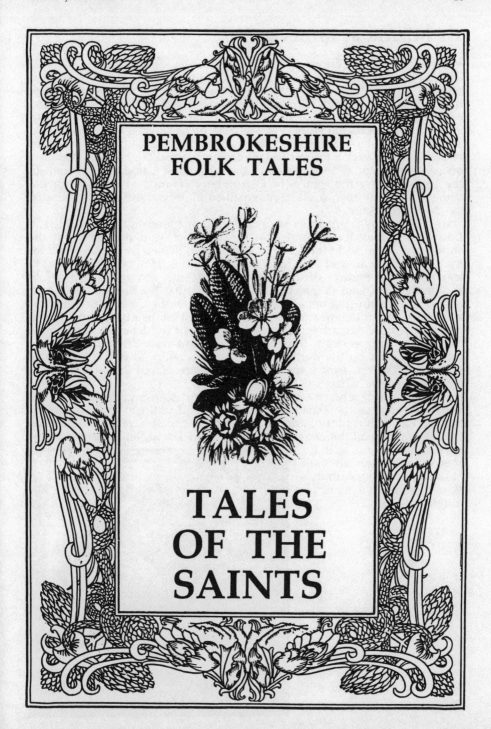

PEMBROKESHIRE
FOLK TALES

TALES
OF THE
SAINTS

1.1 Miracle at Menevia

When Dewi (later to become Dewi Sant or St David) died around the year
588 AD he was buried in the precinct of his monastery, which was often
referred to as Menevia. His remains, together with relics such as his
handbell, his robe and his staff, were preserved by his disciples and
eventually became objects of veneration. However, in the turbulent centuries which followed the church at Menevia or St David's was raided over
and over again by Vikings and other pirates; and then followed centuries
of unrest as the Welsh princes fought each other and the Norman conquer-
ors. As a result of all this upheaval, the relics of St David disappeared. In
the tenth century the monks of Glastonbury claimed to have them; but
some of them, at least, must have remained in or near the church founded
by the patron saint.

In 1081 two Welsh princes swore an oath of friendship on the relics of
Dewi before they fought and won the Battle of Mynydd Carn, but the
shrine was stolen and plundered in 1089. When Bishop Bernard hunted for
the saint's body around 1140 he was unsuccessful. However, according to
legend a great miracle occurred in the thirteenth century. The Prior of
Ewenni had a dream in which it was revealed that the body of Dewi was
buried in a certain spot outside the south porch of the Cathedral. The Prior
was instructed in the dream that the bones must be disinterred and placed
in a new shrine. Accordingly a message was sent to Menevia. Excavations
started, and true enough, the bones of the saint were discovered. A new
recess was built on the north side of the presbytery to house a portable
shrine, and later at least some of the relics were placed in a shrine in the
west wall of the Chapel of the Holy Trinity.

According to legend, the casket behind the cast-iron grille contains the
bones of three saints: David himself, his friend and confessor Justinian,
and the eleventh-century hermit Caradog. The casket is very small, far too
small to contain all the bones of a tall man like David, let alone the bones
of two other men as well. It
was obviously decreed that
St David, like King Arthur,
should be buried in many
different places........

Date: c 1270
Source: N. Rees p 23

*Accordingly a message
was sent to Menevia.*

1.2 The Mystery of St Govan

The little chapel of St Govan is located in one of the most secluded and beautiful spots in Pembrokeshire -- a deep cleft in the limestone cliffs of the south coast, not far from the village of Bosherston. The chapel itself is reputed to be a thirteenth-century replacement of a much earlier building which was a simple hermit's cell.

Who was St Govan? Most probably he was an Irish abbot, sometimes named St Gobhan, who was a contemporary of St David. In old age, maybe around 570 AD, he left his monastery near Wexford and became a missionary in Pembrokeshire. He was something of a recluse, and settled in his primitive cell in the limestone cliffs, where he died around 586 AD. Some people think that Govan was really Queen Cofen, wife of one of the ancient kings of Glamorgan. But the most romantic legend tells that Govan was Sir Gawain, one of the most faithful of King Arthur's Knights of the Round Table. After his encounter with the Green Knight when he was a young man, and after his stirring adventures associated with the Quest for the Holy Grail, it is said that he became a recluse in his old age. Following King Arthur's death, and worn out after a life of chivalry, he sought a place of peace and serenity where he could pass his last years in contemplation. Another version of the old tale tells that he was mortally wounded by Sir Launcelot, went to sea and was shipwrecked on the Pembrokeshire coast. One way or another, he found this cleft in the limestone cliffs, and here he died.

Interestingly enough, there is another tradition from the neighbourhood which refers to Excalibur, the magic sword of King Arthur. It is said that when Arthur died, the sword was flung into the water of a lake, to be caught by a hand which came out of the depths; according to local legend, the place where this happened was Bosherston Pools, no more than a heroic sword's throw from St Govan's Chapel.

Date: c 1050?   *Source: Miles p 186; Hall and Hall p 476*

The little chapel of St Govan is located in one of the most secluded and beautiful spots in Pembrokeshire........

1.3 St. Brynach Comes to Nevern

St Brynach, an Irishman who was rather fond of Pembrokeshire, left a considerable mark on the community through his effective ministry. According to legend, he was a good friend of Dewi Sant, the patron saint of Wales. No less than nine local churches are dedicated to the memory of Brynach. Some of these he founded himself; others were not built until many years after his death. He came to Pembrokeshire in about 540 AD, and stayed for about ten years. After various adventures in Milford and the Gwaun Valley (recounted in **The Last Dragon**, Tales 1.2 and 1.3), Brynach and his little band of disciples travelled towards the north coast, determined to find a place where they could establish a small monastic community.

They made their way to Cilgwyn and then to the banks of the Nevern. There, in a beautiful wooded hollow, they found what appeared to be a good spot for their church and community. So they set to work with a will, cutting trees to make a clearing, carrying the great logs for building, and making the foundations for the church and dwellings. For three solid days they laboured. Then, when they woke up on the fourth day, they found that all traces of their hard work had disappeared; the trees stood thick and silent in the place where they had laboriously hacked out their clearing. Realising that this was a signal from God that this was not the right place, the brothers prayed long and hard for guidance.

Then Brynach was told in a dream that he should go to the confluence of the Nevern River with the little stream called Caman, and should search nearby for a wild white sow with piglets, which would show him where to build his church. So the brothers walked on, looking and listening intently for sight or sound of the wild pigs. Sure enough, they eventually came upon the white sow and her squealing piglets. The animals were not afraid, for Brynach had a special affinity with wild creatures. Quietly the brothers followed the animals through the thick tangled woodland, and at last they stopped in the predestined place. There Brynach and his followers set to work again, and this time the work of felling and building went smoothly until the church and the living quarters were completed.

Date: c 540 AD   *Source : W.J. Rees p 292*

Brynach was told in a dream that he should go to the confluence of the River Nevern.......

1.4 Hospitality at Llanfyrnach

The slate-built church at Llanfyrnach has a medieval tower, and its Victorian embellishments make it look not at all typical of the Welsh-speaking part of Pembrokeshire. However, long before the tower was built there was a smaller and simpler church, and a charming legend reminds us why it was built.

In the middle part of the Sixth Century St Brynach was travelling in the eastern parts of Pembrokeshire on a missionary journey. At last he came to Llanboidy, weary after a long day walking along rough tracks and footpaths. There he found the natives distinctly unfriendly, and it took all his charm to secure a bed for the night on the straw in a cow-shed. When he went on his way, somewhat disgusted, with a stiff neck and straw in his habit, he named the place Llanbeudy, or The Church of the Cow-house. Next he travelled towards Glandwr, where he fared even worse. After a hard day's preaching, he could not even find a little space in a cowshed for the night, and had to sleep huddled under the capstone of the Cilymaenllwyd cromlech, with the cold wind howling around him.

By now the good saint felt that his faith was being sorely tested. But at last he came to another small settlement, where he preached and found a warm welcome among the local people. He was welcomed into the cottage of a poor farmer, who gave him a good hot meal. The farmer and his family talked and laughed long into the evening with Brynach, and then provided him with a warm and comfortable bed for the night. When he set off on his travels again next morning, with his faith in human nature restored, Brynach declared that the place should thenceforth bear his own name. And so the settlement, and its first simple church, came to be known as Llanfyrnach, or the Church of St Brynach.

Date: c 560 AD   *Source : Timmins p 174*

He had to sleep huddled under the capstone of the cromlech......

1.5 The Llawhaden Weather Man

In the strange little church of Llawhaden there is a mutilated effigy of a priest in a recess in the chancel aisle. It is said to be a memorial to St Hugh, a hermit who lived in a cave at Rock Hill. The good saint had a formidable reputation, for he was said to be the first professional Weather Man.

According to legend, St Hugh would spend the first twelve days of each year sitting at the entrance of his cave, contemplating a pool of water and watching the drips fall inexorably from the tangled vegetation and rocky crags above. During this time he ate nothing and spoke to nobody. After this, the hermit was able to foretell the weather for the rest of the year. It was said that he was prepared to write down his weather forecasts on strips of birch-bark. Furthermore, he fully realised the commercial value of his forecasts, which he sold, for a suitable fee, to local farmers. Since he was a good Christian gentleman, it is likely that he asked for gifts of food rather than money. But his weather forecasting service at least enabled him to survive his somewhat spartan lifestyle. No doubt many local farmers were grateful for their local weather forecasting service, and when the saint died they expressed their gratitude by erecting the simple memorial on his tomb in the church.

Date: c 800 AD?   *Source : Miles p 123*

1.6 Caradog and the Castellan

Caradog was a saintly hermit who had his cell not far from Haverfordwest in the early Twelfth Century. According to local tradition, the cell was at a place called Under the Hills, near the present suburb of Merlin's Bridge. No doubt he had moved there for the peace and quiet, having had an adventurous life.

He was born at Brecon, and later became a musician at the court of Rhys ap Tewdwr, the Prince of South Wales. However, he incurred the displeasure of his patron when he lost two prize dogs, and had to flee from the court. He became a pilgrim and eventually took holy orders at the monastery in Llandaff. He settled as a hermit on Barry Island; then moved to Gower; and then tried to settle down on an island off the Pembrokeshire coast. His island retreat was raided by the Normans and by other pirate bands, and so he fled to the mainland, where he hoped that he would be respected both by the Normans and the local Welsh people.

The castellan of Haverfordwest Castle was one Richard Tancard. He had many sons, of whom the youngest was also called Richard. When Richard FitzTancard (literally "son of Tancard") was a child, his father and mother used to send him with parcels of food to Caradog. No doubt they were honourable people, inspired by the desire simply to help an old hermit. But Caradog reciprocated by showering blessings on his benefactors, and he became especially fond of young Richard. According to legend, Caradog blessed the lad and promised him the entire inheritance of his father, including all the portions of his brothers. Richard could hardly believe this, since the youngest sons of large families seldom inherit anything; but for many years he continued his friendship with the old hermit.

When Caradog died in 1124 it was common knowledge that he had asked for his body to be buried at St David's. However, the castellan of Haverfordwest thought he had some claim on it, possibly thinking that he would bury the saintly old man in one of the Haverfordwest churches. So he prevented the bearers from setting off with the body on the road to St David's. Immediately he fell ill, and relented. Next day the party of bearers tried to set out again. For a second time Richard Tancard stopped them, and again he fell ill. Suspecting some divine interference, he relented again and told them they could go. Again he recovered his health, and again he commanded that the party of pall-bearers could not leave the town. So he fell ill for a third time, this time so seriously that he feared for his life. Now he finally called the bearers to his sick-bed and said to them "Go! Go with the body of the old man to St David's before I die. Bury him in the church of St David if you will, and leave me in peace."

This time the party of bearers were allowed to leave the town unmolested, and made their way via Newgale to the shrine of the patron saint. Once he was safely buried, Richard Tancard made a gradual recovery to good health. But strange to relate, Caradog's promise to the son, Richard FitzTancard, was fulfilled. One by one his elder brothers all died, and when his father died in 1130 he was the only one left. So it came to pass that he inherited all his father's lands and estates, and came in turn to be the Castellan of Haverfordwest.

Date: 1124
Sources: Giraldus p 144; Spencer p 20

This time the party of bearers were allowed to leave the town unmolested.

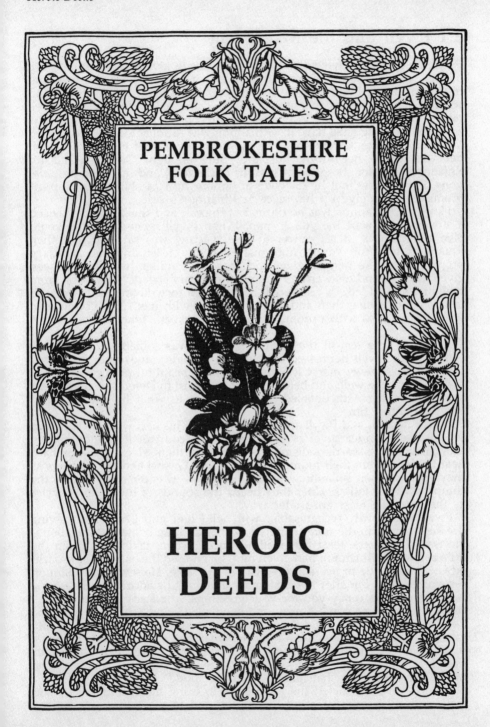

PEMBROKESHIRE
FOLK TALES

HEROIC
DEEDS

2.1 Pwyll and the Magic Bag

Pwyll the Prince of Dyfed was head over heels in love with Rhiannon, but having won her hand in marriage he lost it again before the wedding night. At the wedding feast he had probably had too much to drink, and when a young nobleman entered the hall and asked for a boon Pwyll replied without thinking "Whatever favour you ask of me, so long as it is in my power, you shall have it." Rhiannon was furious, for she recognized the young man as Gwawl, the one chosen by her father Hefeydd, against her will, to be her future husband. Sure enough, Gwawl asked for Rhiannon, and for the place of honour at the feast and marriage preparations. Pwyll knew that by his code of honour he was obliged to keep his promise and to give up his place at Rhiannon's side.

However, Rhiannon was no ordinary princess, and she instantly devised a strategy to thwart the young man. When Pwyll replied that he would give all that was in his power to give, Gwawl was satisfied; but then Rhiannon told the young nobleman that the feast and the marriage preparations were hers to give, and that these things had already been given to Pwyll and his warriors and retainers from Dyfed. "But a year from tonight," she added, "a feast shall be prepared for you and your warriors in this court. Come then and you shall sleep with me." The young man was satisfied, and with a promise to return in a year's time he went on his way.

After this, the rest of the "wedding feast" was something of an anti-climax, with Pwyll depressed by his own stupidity and quite convinced that he would never marry Rhiannon. But the beautiful princess told him that all would be well; and before he left to return to Dyfed she gave him a small magic bag with detailed instructions as to what he should do in twelve months' time.

A year passed, and Pwyll and one hundred of his best warriors travelled on horseback under cover of darkness to the court of Rhiannon. When they arrived, the warriors dismounted and hid themselves in the orchard near the hall. From their hiding place they saw Gwawl and his retainers as they arrived. Then Rhiannon, as beautiful as ever, entered the hall in the company of her father. Later they heard the sounds of music and revelry as the marriage feast got under way.

Pwyll was hardly recognisable, with wild hair and beard and having dressed himself in the rough tattered clothes and rag boots of a vagabond. He waited until the feast was well advanced. Then, taking with him the little bag which Rhiannon had given him, he entered the hall and approached Gwawl and the princess at the head of the table. He saw that Rhiannon recognized him, but after the customary greetings he addressed the young nobleman. "God repay you for your greetings," he said. "I have a small request to make of you." Gwawl felt benevolent, and replied "I welcome your request, stranger. And if you ask me a reasonable boon, I will gladly give it to you." Then Pwyll held out the small bag and said "It is indeed a reasonable request, lord. I ask only that I may ward off hunger. The favour I ask is this small bag full of food." Gwawl replied at once, "That is a most modest request. You shall gladly have the food."

Then Gwawl instructed the attendants to bring meat, and bread, and fruit, and all manner of other foodstuffs, and to place them in the bag which Pwyll held open in front of him. But no matter how much food was placed inside it, it appeared no fuller than before. At last the servants wearied of the task, and Gwawl looked at the bag with amazement. "Friend," he asked, "will your bag never be full?" "Between me and God it will not," replied the whiskered and bedraggled Prince of Dyfed, "until a true nobleman who owns land and dominions shall arise and tread down the food in the bag with both feet, and shall say: Now the bag contains enough!"

At this Rhiannon intervened and said to Gwawl "Brave sir, rise up quickly, for you are such a man." Gwawl rose to the bait, jumped into the bag and began to tread down the food. But immediately the magic bag became larger. Pwyll pulled the top of the bag over Gwawl's head, tipped him over and fastened it with a knot. Then he pulled out a horn from his ragged tunic and blew a loud blast. At this signal, his warriors rushed into the hall and subdued the guests and retainers with ease, for they were in a mellow mood, having eaten and drunk far too much. Pwyll threw off his disguise, and he and his hundred warriors proceeded to play "badger in the bag." The bag, with poor Gwawl inside shrieking for mercy, was kicked and beaten with staves by every man in turn.

At last Hefeydd the Old, Rhiannon's father, intervened, for he was afraid that Gwawl would be killed. "It is not fitting for a nobleman to be slain inside a bag," he said. So Pwyll agreed to stop the game, and promised that he would abide by the decision of Rhiannon and her father concerning the battered young man. Gwawl was in no position to negotiate, and Rhiannon insisted that as a condition of his release he should give up his claim on her and should leave the hall with his chieftains and warriors, never to return. Further, she insisted that he should never lay claim or seek vengeance for what had happened to him. He also had to promise that he would pay sureties as a sign of good intent. And at last, all having been agreed, Gwawl was released from the bag. "I am bruised and wounded and in need of a bath," he complained. "And with your permission I will go on my way."

Covered with indignity, Gwawl mounted his horse and set off for home with his retinue, leaving only a few of his chieftains to pay the sureties and make other arrangements. Soon they set off too, leaving Pwyll and his warriors in full control of the situation. As they had done a year before, they took their places in the hall. Pwyll shaved and cut his hair, and took his place beside his beloved Rhiannon. The minstrels took up their instruments and began to play, and the feasting and drinking recommenced. The evening was passed in singing and laughter, and at last the time came to retire.

A year later than planned, Pwyll and Rhiannon went at last to their bedchamber as man and wife. And there they passed the night in pleasure and contentment.

Date: 800 - 900 AD?   *Source: Jones & Jones p 15*

2.2 The Blind Woman of Haverfordwest

Giraldus Cambrensis and Archbishop Baldwin visited Haverfordwest in 1188 on their mission to obtain Welsh recruits for the Third Crusade. They themselves knew hardly anything about the horrors of the military campaigns, but they made a great impression upon the local people with the power of their preaching. In his book **The Journey Through Wales** Giraldus takes great delight in extolling his own virtues as a preacher and describes how a great crowd of people, including soldiers and civilians, were miraculously affected by his oratory even though he was preaching in Latin and in French, neither of which language they could understand. He says that his listeners were moved to tears and rushed forward in great numbers to receive the sign of the Cross.

There was an old woman in Haverfordwest who had been blind for three years. When she heard that the Archbishop was preaching in the town she sent her son along to the place where the sermon was being delivered, and pleaded with him to bring back something belonging to the Archbishop, even if it was only a thread pulled from his vestments. However, the crowd was so great that the young man could not get anywhere near the Archbishop. He noted where the Archbishop had been standing when he made the sign of the cross, and later on, when the crowds had dispersed, he went to the exact spot and dug up a piece of turf.

When the young man got home with his piece of turf his mother was overjoyed. She knelt down facing the East, prayed to God and pressed the

They themselves knew hardly anything about the horrors of the military campaigns.........

turf to her mouth and eyes. According to Giraldus, so great were her faith and her devotion, and so strong was the miraculous power of the Archbishop, that she was immediately restored to full sight.

Giraldus recorded this story in some detail, and no doubt repeated it on numerous occasions to other crowds and in other locations during the remainder of the journey around Wales. He knew the value of propaganda, and a miracle or two does wonders for an evangelical campaign.......

Date : 1188 *Source: Giraldus p.141*

2.3 The Black Death in Haverfordwest

The plague which struck the town and county of Haverfordwest in 1651-52 was the greatest calamity ever to affect the area, for it reduced the finest trading town in South Wales to acute poverty and distress. The Black Death was probably brought to the town by sailors, and it spread like wildfire. The parish of St Martin's was most sorely infected, and two pest houses were established; one of these was used by the "tarr-coats", men who wore grotesque tarred coats as a primitive form of disinfectant and who collected and buried the corpses and tended the sick. Other premises were secured where comfort could be given to the inflamed and bloated bodies of the dying. The disease killed in three days; hardly anybody who caught it survived.

So many people died or fell ill that the town's markets and fairs were stopped, and the local Guilds complained that their trade had come to a standstill. Some fairs were relocated outside the town. An attempt was made to isolate the townspeople, and the High Constable of Dungleddy issued a warrant preventing anybody from entering or leaving the built-up area. The Mayor complained that the townspeople would starve if food could not be brought in, and common sense prevailed. Food was sent in from all over Pembrokeshire, and received at the Red Gate at the bottom of Holloway.

However, fear stalked the streets and the stench of death was everywhere. Many people moved out into the countryside. Out of the town's population of 3,000, more than half locked up their premises and fled; in May 1652 about 990 poor people were recorded as on the verge of starvation, and when it was all over about 500 of the inhabitants had died. One who died was an eccentric and garrulous old woman referred to in the borough records as Widow Howells, who made a thorough nuisance of herself in the midst of all the chaos. The great hero of the Plague was Rev Stephen Love, the Puritan Rector of St Thomas. He travelled all over the county collecting money and food for the plague victims, visited all the houses where people were ill or where deaths had occurred, and spent much time in the "pest-houses". He won the respect and admiration of everybody; and although he survived the Plague he was worn out by his exertions and died in 1656. Other heroes were Thomas Davids the Mayor and Ben Price the Surgeon, who worked tirelessly for the town as they saw their own families and friends die.

Date: 1651-52 *Sources: James p 51; Worsley p 47*

2.4 Gwilym and the French Champion

Gwilym ap Owen lived in the early years of the Fourteenth Century. He was the youngest of the three sons of Owen ap Robert of Coed Cilrhyd, near Nevern. Owen was a nobleman of some substance, owning extensive territories in the area around Pentre Ifan, Nevern and Brynberian. But he was indecisive, and decreed that when he died his lands should be divided equally between the three sons. The sons would not accept this, and decided that they should fight for the privilege of inheriting the whole of the family estate. So they went into Tycanol Wood, pulled up some oak saplings and made stout staves out of them. Then they climbed up to the rocks above the wood (now called Carnedd Meibion Owen, or the Rocks of the Sons of Owen) and started to fight. The battle was long and bloody, but the boys had enough sense not to kill each other, and decided at last to call it a day without any one of them emerging victorious.

After this Owen decided to settle his lands on the oldest son, and the two younger sons were sent off to be educated. Gwilym went to Oxford and then to the court of the King of England. While he was in London his intelligence and bravery marked him out, and the King took a liking to him. At the time England and France were at war, and Gwilym was invited to join the royal retinue on an expedition to France. A truce was called in the war, and the two royal retinues enjoyed a boisterous evening together. Unfortunately, big trouble appeared in the shape of the French King's champion, Sir Tristan, who started to throw his considerable weight around. He challenged any of his enemies to meet him in personal combat. He was drunk, and the phlegmatic English took no notice; but Gwilym was incensed, and accepted the challenge, believing that the honour of Britain was at stake. A duel ensued, in which Gwilym emerged triumphant. He spared Sir Tristan's life, but he had unwittingly brought the two countries back to the brink of war. The French King protested about the indignity suffered by his champion. The English King apologised profusely, and offered to execute Gwilym for his effrontery and for fighting a duel at a time of truce. Then the French King decided to be magnanimous, saying that this would be a waste of a mighty warrior, and asking instead that Gwilym (who was, after all, a Welshman) should be allowed to join the French court rather than the English one. The English King declined to give up "the doughtiest champion in Christendom", and Gwilym remained loyal; and eventually all concerned were able to laugh about the incident. As a chivalrous gesture the French King even presented Gwilym with the coat of arms of the vanquished Sir Tristan.

When the English retinue returned to London Gwilym was the toast of the City, and from the manner of his defeat of Sir Tristan in personal combat he gained the reputation of being the greatest warrior in the realm. The King made him his personal champion. But Gwilym longed for the leafy and mysterious oakwoods of Tycanol and the wide skies and rocky crags of Carningli, and he asked the King if he might be allowed to return home. Reluctantly the King released him, but rewarded him with an estate in his home territory. So Gwilym, the King's Champion, returned to Cemaes to till the land and hunt the woods and find a wife.

Date: c 1325   *Source: Jones p 70*

2.5 Tragedy on Grassholm

In the first week of December 1893 the schooner **Ellen**, bound for Cardigan with a cargo of Norwegian timber, was forced by heavy weather to put into Milford Haven. When the weather moderated the owner and captain, John Owen, decided that he would proceed for Cardigan. All went well at first, but when the schooner was eight miles from the Bishops a heavy gale blew up again. The captain could make no headway, so he decided to run back to shelter. The vessel shipped some heavy seas, and the five-man crew was kept hard at work on the pumps throughout the night. At last, as the vessel passed Grassholm, all the sails were ripped to shreds by the wind. In the pitch black of the early morning the battered schooner became quite unmanageable, and was driven with great force onto the island.

There were seven men on board. The captain determined at first to stay with the vessel, while the five crew together with the pilot climbed onto the rigging and tried to get onto the safety of the rocks by way of the fore-yard. One of the sailors was swept away and drowned, but the others made it. Bruised and bleeding, they scrambled up onto the island, watching in horror as the **Ellen** broke up before their eyes. They had given up any hope of ever seeing Captain Owen again, but as the storm continued unabated they began to explore in the hope of finding some shelter. Some six hours after the schooner went aground one of the sailors discovered the captain on the rocks, swept by the waves. He was unconscious and bleeding at the mouth. They dragged him to the most sheltered spot they could find, and there they erected a rough shelter with the boards which had come shore from the wreck. The captain drifted in and out of consciousness, asking only for water.

For the whole of the day, and the next night, the men endured the fury of the storm as they waited vainly for some passing vessel to rescue them. At last the steam trawler **Birda** came into view, and her crew spotted the feeble figures waving to them from the island summit. The captain came as close inshore as he dared, for the seas were still very high, and then sent in three men in a small dinghy. Risking all among the wave-washed rocks and fierce currents, the men managed to throw ashore a line and buoy. One by one the shipwrecked mariners flung themselves into the surf and managed to grab the buoy, to be hauled to safety. But they were too weak to help their captain, and indeed they could do nothing to help him had they stayed; so after making him as comfortable as they could they left him in the crude wooden shelter, vowing to return as soon as possible. The **Birda** took the men to Milford Haven, arriving at 3.30 in the afternoon.

Immediately the steam trawler **Her Majesty** set off for Grassholm with the Angle lifeboat in tow. However, the sea was still too rough for anybody to get ashore, and after making repeated attempts through the evening and throughout the night the rescue attempt had to be called off. The vessels returned to Milford. After twenty-four hours the sea had gone down a little, and the **Her Majesty** set off again. This time the captain managed to get a party ashore, but when they arrived they found that the crude hut had blown down. Inside it they found the body of Captain Owen. He had been dead about twelve hours.

Date: 1893 *Source: Howells p 162*

2.6 The Wreck of the SS Molesey

In November 1929 the cargo ship **Molesey** was steaming from Manchester to Cardiff in water ballast, with 36 people on board. She ran into bad weather near the Bishops and the captain decided to put in to Milford Haven for shelter. But he had left it too late; the vessel was high out of the water, and a 70 mph gale was blowing. Then, off Skokholm, the steering gear failed, and after rigging some sails on the mainmast the captain decided that he had no option but to run through Jack Sound.

On entering the Sound the ship kept on going broadside, and the captain put out the anchors. But so fierce was the hurricane that the anchor chains snapped, and the vessel was swept onto the rocks of Midland Isle. The seas were the worst that local people had ever seen, and they swept right over the wreck as she lay helpless on the rocks. The captain's bridge was carried away, and the superstructure soon began to disintegrate. Seven of the ship's company were swept away and drowned. The terrified survivors huddled into the chart-room to await their fate, and they were amazed to see two white-faced boys emerge from the forecastle, where they had stowed away in Manchester. They hauled them into the chart-room and gave them lifejackets.

As the ship filled with water it was feared that the boilers would explode, and three volunteers went below to rake out her fires. The wireless operator stuck to his post, sending out a stream of SOS signals, and eighteen distress rockets were fired. Early on, a signal was picked up and the Angle lifeboat went out through mountainous seas to Skomer. It searched for a wreck to no avail, and had to return to base. But signals were still being received, and it went out again in the pitch darkness. Again it failed to locate the **Molesey** and returned to Angle. At daybreak it went out again, with waves washing right over it. At last it located the wreck, and the coxwain, James Watkins, was able to get close under its stern. He swept in and out on the waves and took 28 people off.

The heroism of the crew of the Angle lifeboat was matched by many others that night. Old William Morris of Marloes called for six volunteers and set out from Martin's Haven in a small open boat; he approached the wreck in Jack Sound, but on seeing the Angle lifeboat he turned back, knowing that the lifeboat had a much better chance of affecting a rescue. The St David's lifeboat also set out to try and help, and had to battle across St Bride's Bay against fearsome seas in order to reach Jack Sound. The brave crew searched for the **Molesey** all night along the cliffs of Skomer, coming as close as they dared and swamped continuously by the waves. After a thirteen-hour ordeal the St David's crew found the wreck just as the Angle lifeboat was taking off the last survivors, including an old man with two broken legs. Afterwards many of those who had taken part in the rescue received awards and commendations.

A full day after the rescue a Maltese crew member was spotted wandering about on Skomer Island. Later he explained that he had been fast asleep while the others were being rescued. When he woke up he was quite convinced that he was the only survivor, and since the sea had gone down somewhat he had swum across to Skomer to look for help!

Date: 1929   *Sources: Howells p 164; Bennett p 54*

2.7 The Celestial Dragon at St David's

Geoffrey of Monmouth is chiefly famous for an extremely unreliable volume called **The History of the Kings of Britain**, written around 1140. Some of it is based on fact, but a great deal of it is fiction; but it was one of the first literary best-sellers, and it had a great influence upon later writers who were intent upon exploring the Arthurian legend. What follows is a greatly abbreviated version of one of Geoffrey's heroic tales, in which Menevia or St David's figures prominently.

With the help of his brother Uther and Merlin the Magician, King Aurelius Ambrosius transported a "Giant's Ring" of stones from Mount Killaraus in Ireland to Stonehenge, where it was re-erected as a monument to dead heroes. Then a great feast was held, lasting three days. However, not everybody celebrated, for Ambrosius had made two deadly enemies. One was Paschent, a son of the wicked king Vortigern, intent upon revenge for the death of his father at the hands of Ambrosius; and the other was Gillomanius, an Irish warrior whose army had been defeated while trying to prevent the export of the Giant's Ring. Paschent attacked Ambrosius with a German army but was defeated and had to flee to Ireland. There he made an alliance with Gillomanius. The two men, driven by hatred, fitted out a new army and a fleet of sailing ships. Then their invasion force set out across St George's Channel and landed at Porth-clais, near Menevia (St David's) in Pembrokeshire.

News of the invasion soon reached Ambrosius, who was at that time lying ill in Winchester. Since he was not well enough to take command of his army, he dispatched it towards Pembrokeshire under the leadership of his brother Uther Pendragon. News of the King's illness reached Paschent and Gillomanius, who became convinced that their army of Saxons and Irishmen could now go on to conquer the whole kingdom. While they were discussing the tactics for their military campaign, a Saxon called Eopa asked if he could speak to them. He was shown into their tent, and immediately asked "How much will you give to the man who kills Aurelius Ambrosius for you?" Paschent replied "If only I could find a man to do that, I would give him a thousand pounds of silver and my own lifelong friendship. And if I become king of this island, I promise on oath that I will make him a captain of my army." This satisfied Eopa, who then explained that he could speak the British language as well as a native, and that he knew the habits of the people. So he set off for Winchester, promising that he would assassinate the king with a potion of poison.

Then Eopa shaved off his beard and disguised himself as a monk. He collected an assortment of bottles and filled them with potions, and when he arrived at Winchester he presented himself immediately at the court of Ambrosius. "I am a man of God and also a doctor," he lied. "I hear that the King is ill, and I am sent by God to bring him back to health again." He was shown into the bedchamber, where he asked the King if he could prepare a medicine which would cure him of his fever. "Yes, yes," replied the King from his bed. "Mix your potion, good doctor. I am in your hands." So Eopa mixed the poison and gave it to the King, who swallowed it in one gulp. "Now, my Lord," said the assassin, "You must snuggle down under your bed-cover and sleep. And when you awake, you will be restored to full health so that you may resume your royal duties." With that the King obediently pulled his bed-cover over his head while the royal servants, accompanied by Eopa, crept silently from the room. And so the great King died in his sleep. Before the crime was discovered Eopa slipped away from the court and was lost in the crowd, to make his way back to Menevia.

At the moment of the King's death in Winchester, a strange and terrible vision was seen in the skies above South Wales. A huge new star (probably a meteor or comet) was seen, with a single beam of light shining from it. At the end of the beam there was a great ball of fire, spread out in the shape of a dragon. From the dragon's mouth there extended two rays of brilliant light, one extending towards Gaul and the other towards Ireland. Just then Uther Pendragon and his army were in Dyfed, hunting for the invasion force of Paschent and Gillomanius. The men of both armies, and their leaders, were terrified by the vision of the celestial dragon in the skies overhead. The dragon reappeared in the skies on three successive nights, and Uther decided at last that it was an omen. Merlin the Wizard was with the army, and Uther summoned him and asked him to explain the significance of the vision. Merlin wept, and explained through his tears that Ambrosius was dead. "We, the people of Britain, are orphaned," he said. "By the death of our King we shall all die, unless God helps us. But hasten on with the army, Uther Pendragon! Victory is yours, and you will be king of all Britain. The star is yours, and yours is the dragon. One of the beams of light is your son, who will be a mighty ruler in his time. The other beam of light is your daughter, whose sons and daughters will be kings of Britain one after the other."

In spite of his grief Uther urged his army on, for he was now but half a day's march from Menevia. And so the two armies met, somewhere in North Pembrokeshire. The battle was as fierce as any in the history of the heroes of Britain, and went on for most of the day. But at last the army of Uther was victorious; thousands of the enemy were slain, including Paschent and Gillomanius. The rebels who survived attempted to flee back to their ships at Porth-clais, but they were pursued and cut down, one by one, by the victorious Britons.

Uther Pendragon, having avenged the murder of his brother, returned with all possible haste to Winchester. There he saw the body of Ambrosius, and after a great state funeral the dead King was buried in the middle of the Giant's Ring at Stonehenge. Then Uther was appointed King in his stead. Because of the celestial dragon which had appeared over Menevia Uther had two golden dragons made by the best goldsmiths in the land. One of them was presented to the congregation of the cathedral church of Winchester; and the other became Uther's personal symbol and talisman, to be carried with him into battle and on his journeys of state. And this is how Uther came to be known as "Pendragon", and how the dragon came to be the symbol of the British people.

Date: c 450 AD?   *Source: Geoffrey of Monmouth p 200*

PEMBROKESHIRE FOLK TALES

STRANGE HAPPENINGS

3.1 Family Trouble at Nevern Castle

Most of us are used to a spot of family trouble now and then, but if we want an example of domestic problems on a grand scale we need look no further than Nevern Castle. Nowadays there is little left on the site but a few traces of motte and bailey earthworks, a strange ditch, and a collapsed stone tower. These features all date from the Twelfth Century, which was a time of broken oaths and dark deeds.

The motte and bailey castle was built by the Norman Robert Martin (Martin de Tours) in the early part of the Twelfth Century, probably as the original stronghold for the Barony of Cemaes. Towards the end of the century the most powerful leader in Wales was Rhys ap Gruffydd, otherwise known as "The Lord Rhys". He was a clever politician as well as a great military leader, and he forged an alliance with King Henry which allowed relative peace in South Wales but which caused great resentment among his violent sons. In one of his astute moves he gave his daughter Angharad in marriage to William FitzMartin, who was then the Baron of Cemaes. The couple lived contentedly enough at Nevern Castle, and Rhys vowed on all the sacred relics that he would leave them there in peace and quiet. However, the death of Henry in 1189 was followed by a period of political upheaval, during which Rhys revolted against the crown. Breaking all his oaths at the instigation of his "cunning and artful" son Gruffydd, he attacked his own son-in-law at Nevern in 1191, seized the Castle and evicted the young couple. Rhys then gave the Castle to Gruffydd, breaking another oath in the process.

Relations between Rhys and his sons were strained at the best of times, and three years later Rhys evicted Gruffydd and installed Maelgwyn instead. By now Rhys was finding it difficult to control his unruly brood and he planned to disinherit his own daughter, his grandsons and his two granddaughters. There followed a battle with his sons Maelgwyn and Hywel, during which Rhys was captured and imprisoned in Nevern Castle. It was probably at this time that the inner castle at Nevern was built, with a stone tower protected by a deep ditch cut into the bedrock. Rhys was locked up in the stone tower for the greater part of a year. However, during yet another family feud, Hywel turned against his brother, burned the Castle and released his father. After this the attentions of the Lord Rhys and his feuding sons seem to have been diverted elsewhere; the damaged castle was abandoned by this unruly Welsh family, never to be re-occupied. As for William and Angharad, they built a new and more desirable castle at Newport and apparently lived there happily ever after.

Date : 1191   *Source: Geraldus Cambrensis p 170*

3.2 The Lucky Golden Dollar

One of the best-known of Llangwm characters in the early part of the century was Captain George Morgans. He was of good Llangwm stock, although at the time of his birth in 1877 his parents were living in St Dogmael's. His father was a coastguard, and from an early age young George was determined to go to sea. He enlisted at the age of sixteen on a square-rigged trading vessel, and worked his way up to First Mate by the time he was 23 years old.

At some time during the early part of his career an extraordinary incident made a deep impression on young George. He was working on the deck of a sailing cargo ship during a terrible storm when a huge wave engulfed the ship and washed him overboard. As he struggled in the water he was convinced that he had no hope of survival, but almost immediately a second huge wave picked him up and deposited him once again on the ship's deck. Not too sure whether he was alive or in Heaven, he managed to scramble to safety. In his pocket at the time was a crude leather purse containing a golden five-dollar coin which he had obtained on a trading visit to the United States. George convinced himself that the purse and its gold coin were a sort of talisman which would ensure his safety at sea, and thereafter he always kept it in his pocket when he was on duty.

After transferring to steam ships around the turn of the century George Morgans became a Master Mariner at the age of 26, and enjoyed an eventful career on all the oceans of the world. He was a small and rather fragile-looking man, but his adventures during the First World War did not appear to damage his health. After the War he often came back to Llangwm to see the family, which was a large one bound by very close ties. At last fate caught up with him, but he did not die at sea. In 1927 he was taken ill on board his ship and was ferried ashore to a hospital in Algiers. There, far from home, he died and was buried; but the family paid for his coffin to be exhumed and brought back to Llangwm, where in the following year there was a full funeral followed by re-burial.

The lucky purse with its American five-dollar piece was looked after by the family, and it was passed on to the next member of the family to go to sea. This was Glyn Morgan, a nephew of the old sea captain who joined the Royal Navy in 1940, in the dark days of the Second World War. At that time his chances of survival could not have been great, for German U-boats seemed to have Allied shipping at their mercy. In December 1940 the young Llangwm rating was on board the ship **Galatea** off Cyrenaica when it was hit by a torpedo fired by a German submarine. The ship went down very quickly, and almost the whole complement of 600 seamen were lost. Glyn had his uncle's old purse with its lucky coin in his back pocket as he leapt into the oily water. He managed to struggle away from the vortex of the sinking ship, and found a piece of floating wreckage. For four and a half hours he hung on and kept himself afloat, repeatedly checking that the purse was still there in his pocket and praying fervently that it would bring him deliverance just as it had once delivered his old uncle. At last he was picked up by another vessel; and he survived the war to become a well-loved teacher.

Date: 1940   *Source: Thomas p 21*

3.3 The Legend of The Huntsman's Leap

A short distance to the west of St Govan's Chapel on the south coast of Pembrokeshire there is a fearsome chasm in the limestone cliffs caused by the erosion of the sea along a narrow fault-line. The chasm is about 120 feet deep and only a few yards wide; in rough weather it echoes with the sound of the waves as they are confined and compressed by the vertical rock walls. Until you are almost on top of the chasm you do not even know it is there, and it still presents a great danger to walkers in bad weather. There is an old legend behind its name. Once upon a time the local hunt was out on the cliffs, with the hounds in hot pursuit of a fox. The hunt had a new member who was unfamiliar with the local terrain, and he was left some way behind the chase. As he galloped up he saw fox, horses and hounds not far ahead; but he did not know that all of them had just completed a detour around a deep chasm in the cliffs. He rode straight ahead, going towards the chasm at full tilt. At the last moment both he and his horse saw it, and since it was far too late to stop the horse soared into the air and landed safely on the other side. Having had a considerable shock the rider reined in his horse, dismounted, and went back to look at the chasm which he had just cleared; but as soon as he gazed down more than a hundred feet to the roaring foam below he suffered from a heart attack and dropped down dead. Thereafter the chasm became known as The Huntsman's Leap.

Date: c 1800?   *Source: Mr David James*

......there is a fearsome chasm in the limestone cliffs caused by the erosion of the sea along a narrow fault-line.

3.4 The Matrons of Cardigan

In the year 1188 Giraldus Cambrensis accompanied Archbishop Baldwin on a journey around Wales, preaching to the masses and seeking to gain support in Wales for the Third Crusade. An account of his adventures is contained in the famous book entitled **The Journey Through Wales**. The book contains records of many wonders and mysteries, and tells us a great deal not only about Giraldus himself but also about the superstitions and beliefs of the common people of the Twelfth Century. When the two clerics arrived in Cardigan and commenced their mission they were greeted with enthusiasm by the local people. Many men were encouraged to take the Cross and to join the Crusade. One of those who did so was the only son of an old woman who depended on him totally since she was not in the best of health. The old woman did not resent the prospect of losing her son, and indeed she was inspired to say "Jesus Christ, our most dear Lord, I give you heartfelt thanks for having judged me worthy to bear a son whom you have deigned to accept into your service." Giraldus was greatly impressed by this show of simple faith.

Not everybody reacted to the mission in quite the same way, and Giraldus describes a terrible retribution which was visited upon another woman of the same town who resisted the divine call. This woman was referred to by Giraldus as "one of the Matrons of Cardigan." As the Men of God were preaching to the crowds on the Town Square, she noticed that her husband was greatly affected by their oratory. Furthermore, he was showing a distinct inclination to sign up for the Crusade. She seized him firmly by the cloak and the belt, and then in full view of everyone watching she brazenly prevented him from going up to the Archbishop and taking the Cross. Giraldus was not impressed.

Three nights later the woman had a terrible nightmare in which she heard an awesome voice speaking to her. The voice said "You have taken my servant away from me. Therefore the thing you hold most dear shall be taken away from you." The woman woke up in a cold sweat and woke her husband who was lying beside her. She related her vision to him and they both became convinced that something fearsome was about to happen.

Their little boy was woken up by all the commotion and sensed that all was not well. To comfort him the parents took him into their own bed. Eventually all three managed to get back to sleep. However, as they slept the mother rolled on top of the poor little boy. He was suffocated, and when the parents woke in the morning he was dead.

The parents were naturally distraught by this turn of events, but immediately the husband went to the local Bishop and told him about his wife's dream and about the "punishment" visited upon them by God. Although Giraldus and Archbishop Baldwin had by then moved on, he took the Cross and committed himself to the Third Crusade. His poor wife was unable to make any further objection and Giraldus relates (clearly with some satisfaction) that she sewed the sign of the Cross onto her husband's tunic with her own trembling hands.

Date : 1188   *Source: Giraldus p 172*

3.5 Romance at St Bride's Mansion

The present St Bride's Castle is an eccentric mansion built around 1830 in the grand style by Lord Kensington. There was an earlier mansion on the same site. However, the original St Bride's Mansion was located much closer to St Bride's Haven, with walled gardens, fishponds and even a bowling green. The walled gardens still exist, but the house is now an ivy-covered ruin.

There is a romantic tale about the old house and the old family. Early in the fifteenth century there was a terrible storm which caused the wreck of a merchant ship out in St Bride's Bay. Jane, the young daughter of Sir John de St Bride's, went for a walk down to the beach, with the wild wind howling about her and the waves crashing onto the rocky shore. Her attention was attracted by something in the waves, and on approaching she realised that it was a young man clinging onto some debris from the wrecked ship. She rushed into the water and managed to drag him ashore, at which point he lost consciousness. He was clearly close to death. Jane rushed back to the house and called some of the servants to come and help; and together they carried the young man to warmth and safety.

They took off his sodden clothes and put him into a dry warm bed, but for many days his life was in the balance. Jane made it her duty to keep watch over the shipwrecked mariner as he suffered from bouts of fever. Night after night she sat at his bedside, holding his hand and mopping his brow. But gradually he began to recover. He said that his name was Thomas Laugharne, and that he could hardly believe his good fortune when he opened his eyes and saw his angel of deliverance. He came from a simple family, and had been intent upon a career as a seaman. He was a good-looking young man, and as a consequence of the ordeal they had been through he and his young nurse began to forge a strong bond of friendship. Soon they were "head over ears" in love with each other, and in due course they were married.

So was founded the "lucky" Laugharne dynasty. Thomas and Jane were set up by the young lady's father in the house of Orlandon, not far from St Bride's. They produced a large family which survived for many generations as one of the leading families of Pembrokeshire. The good fortune of the young man's rescue from the arms of death continued in the family for about 300 years; and the Laugharnes were said always to be "fortunate in their nuptials".

One of the most famous members of the family was Col. Rowland Laugharne, the Parliamentarian commander who routed the Royalists at the Battle of Colby Moor in 1645. The luck of the family was certainly with him three years later, when he, together with Mayor John Poyer and Col. Rice Powell, having switched to the Royalist cause, were sentenced to death as renegade leaders. As recounted in Story 2.7 in **Pembrokeshire Folk Tales**, two of the renegades were reprieved by the drawing of lots; Poyer was executed by a firing-squad while Laugharne and Powell were given slips carrying the words "Life given by God".

Date: c 1420   *Sources: Davies p 6, Miles p 160*

3.6 Insurrection at Fishguard

During the Rebecca Riots in Pembrokeshire (1839 - 1844) the anger of the rural population was directed against the owners of the Turnpike Trusts which had been set up as part of a privatised road-building programme. In theory, the income from Trust toll-gates was supposed to be used for building new roads and improving old ones; but lack of proper regulation of the Trusts resulted in too many toll-gates, tolls which were far too high for the rural population to afford, and widespread corruption. At a time of terrible hardship on the land, the poor people of Pembrokeshire rebelled, and the resulting Rebecca Riots have entered into local folk-lore. The main task of the rioters was the destruction of toll-gates, and the men involved always dressed in women's clothes and referred to themselves as "Rebecca's Daughters".

Some Turnpike Trusts attracted more fury from the rioters than others. One of the most notorious was the Fishguard Trust, which was guilty of the most blatant maladministration and corruption. After many months of simmering discontent on the part of local farmers and cottagers, things came to a head in August 1843.

To start with, about 300 men from the area around Wolfscastle and Little Newcastle converged on the Corner Piece Inn on the Fishguard - Haverfordwest road. After consuming copious quantities of ale they set out to destroy the Prendergast gate, at the northern limit of Haverfordwest, which had been put up by the Fishguard Trust in an illegal position. The operation was a shambles, for not only were the men drunk, but the leadership of the appointed Rebecca left something to be desired. He set off to do a reconnaissance, leaving the gang in the charge of a youngster named Davies, with whom he left his double-barrelled shotgun. Before their leader returned the men decided to set off for Prendergast, blissfully unaware that a spy had informed the authorities of their imminent arrival. In high spirits they set off down the road, all with blackened faces and wearing ill-fitting women's clothes. Young Davies, who had a horse, was so keen that he soon left the rest of the men far behind; and waving his gun in the air and making a terrible noise, he rode straight into the ambush. In the pitch darkness there followed a confused and chaotic battle in which young Davies' gun went off, killing one of the rioters' own horses. All escaped except two young lads, who were later brought to trial.

In mid-September one of the most audacious assaults ever mounted by Rebecca took place in Fishguard. There were two toll-gates in the neighbourhood, one in the town and the other at Penmorfa. The gate-keepers were universally hated, not only by the farmers and cottagers but also by the townspeople; and they were given many warnings by Rebecca and her daughters. They ignored these warnings, and the blows and the curses of the locals, and got their just desserts when Rebecca and her daughters arrived at midnight on Friday 8 September and smashed down the two gates. The gate-keepers were warned that if they continued to take tolls Rebecca would return on Monday and would smash down their houses as well. True to her word, and having given adequate warning, she came back on Monday with 600 followers, riding into town with guns firing and drums beating and trumpets blowing. The rioters were cheered on by the townspeople, since there was no sign of magistrates or constables any-

where. The gang was noisy but well disciplined; and with the enthusiastic support of the locals Rebecca ordered the gate-keepers to remove all their belongings from their houses before they were reduced to piles of rubble.

Then the rioters roamed the streets, and for three hours Fishguard was ruled by Rebecca. Law and order effectively broke down as the rioters hunted for victims who were known to be associated in any way with the Fishguard Trust. One Henry Collins had his house blasted by gunfire, and the Trust's surveyor, John McKenna, had his garden wall levelled to the ground. Eventually Rebecca and her daughters moved off, leaving about three thousand cheering people (almost the whole population of the town) in the market square.

The repercussions of the insurrection in Fishguard were many and varied. The Vice-Lieutenant of the County was furious, but he knew that the authorities had lost all the respect of the townspeople of Fishguard. He wrote to the Home Secretary asking for a garrison of troops to be stationed in the town, since the magistrates were in dread of drawing down the vengeance of the townspeople on their heads. The Home Secretary was even more furious, refusing the request for troops and instructing the magistrates and other civil authorities to take appropriate action to apprehend the rioters. A reward was offered, together with a promise of immunity from prosecution for any rioter who would betray his colleagues. Nothing happened for two months, but then one Thomas Williams bid for the reward and swore a statement naming 33 of the rioters. All 33 were arrested and placed in jail, and when they appeared before the magistrates in Fishguard Town Hall there was pandemonium in the angry crowd, which had to be kept at bay by three ranks of Royal Marines with fixed bayonets.

Seven of the prisoners were discharged, and the rest were committed on bail to stand trial at the next Assize Court. However, there was no evidence against them other than the testimony of Thomas Williams, and no matter how hard they tried the authorities could find nobody else to support the prosecution case. At the Assizes, inevitably, the Crown offered no evidence and all the men were freed, much to the delight of the people of Fishguard. As for Thomas Williams, he and his wife had to be locked in Haverfordwest Gaol for their own protection. At last they were given £20 by the Home Office, smuggled out of town and sent in great secrecy to Aberystwyth, where it was felt that they could start a new life.

Date: 1843   *Source: Molloy p 177*

3.7 The Mystery of the Hirlas Horn

One of the great moments of pageantry at the Welsh National Eisteddfod occurs when the Archdruid receives the Hirlas Horn (*Y Corn Hirlas*) from a local matron, symbolising the hospitable offering of mead or wine to a welcome guest. The Eisteddfod Hirlas Horn is a ceremonial and very elaborate artifact commissioned and made in late Victorian times; but other drinking horns have featured prominently in Welsh history, and in Pembrokeshire one particular horn has strong associations with Henry Tudor and the march to Bosworth Field in 1485.

The Hirlas Horn of Stackpole Court was one of the great treasures of Baron Cawdor and the Campbell family. During the 1800's it was kept at the elegant mansion of Stackpole Court. It was sixteen inches in length, mounted in silver and supported by two animals, namely a dragon and a greyhound, which were the supporters of the arms of the house of Tudor. Its origins are shrouded in mystery. According to tradition Henry stayed on August 9th at the house of Dafydd ab Ifan at Llwyndafydd near New Quay before striking northwards and eastwards with his army across the centre of Wales. Later, after the defeat of Richard III at the Battle of Bosworth Field, when Henry was safely installed as King of England, he sent the fine drinking horn to Dafydd as a sign of gratitude for the hospitality he had received.

However, things may not have been quite so simple. Another story relates that the horn was in fact a christening present to a son born to Dafydd's daughter as a result of the royal visit. The royal offspring eventually became aware of his parentage, and the royal descendants are still alive and well in Ceredigion. As for the Hirlas Horn, it remained in the family of Dafydd ab Ifan for almost 300 years, after which it passed by marriage to the family of Richard Vaughan of Golden Grove and thence to the Campbells of Stackpole Court in 1804.

Date: 1485   *Sources: Miles p 189, Hall and Hall p 472*

3.8 Close Shave at Robeston Wathen

During the Seventeenth Century the roads of Pembrokeshire were notoriously dangerous, not only because they were poorly built but also because of robbers and highwaymen. There was no police force, so law enforcement left much to be desired. There was no regulation of inns, and so travellers were often at the mercy of unscrupulous innkeepers who worked with criminals to relieve them of their valuables. It was not unknown for travellers to be beaten up or even murdered simply for the sake of their possessions.

Many of the "inns of ill repute" were known to regular travellers, who kept well clear of them. But things were not so easy for long-distance travellers who had to call at the nearest convenient inn when they were overtaken by darkness. One notorious inn was The Three Lords near Pendine, and there was another one near Robeston Wathen. One day around 1810 Mr James, who farmed at Cadno near Pendine, was travelling on horseback from Cwm (Lower Town, Fishguard) to Carmarthen. He was carrying with him a substantial amount of money, and he had with him a pack-horse which was laden with luggage. He passed Haverfordwest, but night began to draw in, and as he approached Robeston Wathen he had to look for accommodation for the night. He saw the lights of an inn, and although he did not particularly like the look of the establishment or its proprietor he checked in, unloaded his baggage and stabled his two horses.

He was shown to his room, but immediately felt uneasy, aware that the innkeeper and his wife were showing an uncommon interest in his baggage. Also, some of the other "clients" in the bar room downstairs looked as if they were more familiar with the inside of a prison than the inside of a gentleman's mansion.

Later, when the heavy drinking was well under way in the bar room, with the inn keeper and his wife hard at work, Mr James took the opportunity to investigate some of the other rooms. Taking a lantern in his hand, he opened one or two doors and found nothing suspicious; but then he found a locked door, and on peeping through the gaps in the planking he saw a room illuminated by the faint light of the moon. There was a table in the middle of the floor, and he was horrified to see that it was covered with pistols, knives and swords.

Deciding that the inn was used by a band of robbers and immediately fearing for his life, Mr James decided to escape. He packed up his baggage, and crept down the back stairway, freezing and holding his breath every time a step creaked. But the sounds of revelry continued in the bar room, and he began to feel that he would make good his escape. Soon he was out through the back door and into the yard. He found his way in the moonlight to the stable, and saddled up his riding horse, with his heart pounding and a cold sweat on his forehead lest any of the gang should see him. He led the two horses out into the yard, and started to fix his luggage onto the pack animal's flanks.

Just then the door of the inn opened and the yard was flooded with light. There, standing in the doorway, was the innkeeper, looking none too amused. Almost petrified with fear, Mr James climbed onto his horse's back and shouted to the man "I expected my servant to have been here by

And with that he galloped out of the yard and away down the road,
with the innkeeper shouting after him.

now; he must have missed the inn. I must be off to find him!'' And with
that he galloped out of the yard and away down the road, with the
innkeeper shouting after him.

When the fugitive had gone a little way he heard a "peculiar kind of
whistle" which he knew was used to confuse horses, but he managed to
keep the animals going. Later he stopped and listened intently, and heard
the sound of horses' hooves behind him in the distance. He knew that he
was being pursued, and so he urged his horses to a gallop again, and kept
going in the moonlight until he reached the safety of Narberth. He was
exhausted and still trembling with fear, but in the town he managed to
find a good and reputable inn where he was well looked after.

In later years Mr James told this story to his grandchildren, and he
remained convinced for the rest of his life that he had been lucky to escape
in one piece from the robbers of Robeston Wathen.

Date: c 1810   *Source: Curtis p 284*

3.9 The Arrival of Alice Williams

In 1927 a young man named Ronald Lockley arrived on the island of Skokholm to find it deserted and derelict. He managed to take out a long lease, and he lived there with his family until 1940, when the dangers of the Second World War forced them to move to the mainland.

Before his wife Doris came out to the island Ronald was helped by John, a local fisherman, as he struggled to make the old farm buildings habitable. The two of them had a fearsome task, for the walls were crumbling, the windows broken, and the roof full of holes. In the winter of 1927-28 they began to wonder whether, with virtually no building materials to hand, they would ever make the farm weather-proof as the gales roared in, one after another, from the west. Then, one day towards the end of February, **Alice Williams** arrived on the island. She was a two-masted wooden schooner, and she arrived on the high tide like a phantom out of the fog, with all sails set and with not a soul on board. Ronald discovered her wedged into a cove beneath Spy Rock, on the east side of the island. She was high and dry, and had clearly been driven in during the night, when there had been a strong south-easterly wind blowing. As the fog cleared and the sea calmed, Ronald and John boarded her, to discover that she was badly holed, with the sea washing in and out of her hold and cabin.

The two men decided that she had been abandoned at sea, and that she was well and truly a wreck. They scrambled onto the deck, which was a confusion of ropes and chains. There was wreckage floating everywhere in the sea, and most of the contents of the cabin and sail-room had already been washed away; the panelling and furniture were smashed, and planks and timber had been cast by the waves into disorderly heaps. There was little of value to be seen, but the hold was full of two hundred tons of good quality coal. The rudder had broken off and was visible among the red sandstone boulders washed by the tide, and the wheel-shaft had broken off near the rudder-post. As soon as the men realised that the ship could not be saved they took down the sails, cut them free of the masts, and rigged up a makeshift winch by means of which they raised the heavy canvas to the clifftop.

Before they left the wreck for the day the two men made a wonderful discovery, for there, drifting to and fro in the flotsam and jetsam near the battered hull, they discovered Alice Williams herself. She had a strong, bright face with piercing blue eyes, and neatly coiled raven hair bound with a black ribbon and red roses. She wore a white frock with an old-fashioned tight bodice, and around her neck there was a rosary of jet and a black cross. In spite of the fact that she had one arm missing, she was a serene and proud figure, dressed in the fashion of the mid-Victorian era. With some difficulty the men managed to catch her with a grappling-hook, and they hauled her onto the deck of the stricken vessel. Later they carried her up to a position overlooking South Haven. There she stayed, as proud a figure-head as ever was made, to survey the scene while the men decided what to do next.

On the following day Ronald and John went ashore at Marloes, and after a short time on the telephone Ronald discovered that the **Alice Williams** had been abandoned in the night by her crew of five after losing her headsails and dragging her anchor. They had been picked up safely by a trawler near St Ann's Head. Ronald immediately bought the wreck for £5, excluding anchors and chains. He managed to return to the island next day with a small group of willing helpers, and over the course of a week of unremitting toil they managed to save most of the coal, ropes, fittings, wheelhouse and cook's galley, and much of the planking. But the waves and tides took their toll with every day that passed, and at last the brave vessel was totally destroyed in a south-easterly gale. The wind and sea piled her timbers high on the island beaches, and Ronald and his helpers managed to save many of these for the reconstruction work on the farm.

And so **Alice Williams** providentially helped in the restoration of the Skokholm farmhouse and out-buildings, and also provided enough coal to keep the new settlers warm for many years. To this day the brightly-painted lady rescued from the sea looks down upon South Haven with an enigmatic smile on her face, watching the comings and goings of those who love the red sandstone island and its wildlife.

 Date: 1927 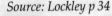 *Source: Lockley p 34*

3.10 The Bleeding Yews of Nevern

In Nevern Churchyard, as in all the best churchyards, there are a number of very ancient yew trees lining the path from the gate to the church porch. They cast a cool green shade over the lichen-covered gravestones, and their gnarled and twisted forms have inspired many artists and poets over the centuries. However, the most interesting feature of the yew trees is that several of them drip a rich red sap from areas where the bark has been damaged in the past. One of them in particular releases a more or less continuous flow of "blood" from an ancient wound. This particular tree has been an object of curiosity and even veneration for as long as people can remember, and it is perhaps inevitable that it should have its own particular legend. One version has it that the yew tree bleeds for the sins of the world, and will bleed continuously until goodness takes the place of evil. According to another version, the tree will bleed until a Welsh prince again resides in Nevern Castle. And a third version states that long ago, when there was a monastery here, a monk was wrongly hanged from the branches of the tree for a crime he did not commit. As the noose was slipped around his neck, he cried out that from the day of his death the tree would bleed for ever as a testimony to his innocence.

Date: c 700 AD? *Source: word of mouth*

3.11 Maenclochog and the Bouncing Bomb

About a mile from Maenclochog there is a fine tunnel built for the Maenclochog Railway around the year 1876. The tunnel is in a reasonable state of repair, and it is still visited occasionally by railway buffs intent upon following the route of the old railway line.

Few of the visitors to the tunnel realise that it played a key role in the history of the Second World War. During the War much of the area around Rosebush and Maenclochog was occupied by the armed forces, and many of the activities of the military were shrouded in secrecy. On various occasions the old railway line was used by the RAF for target practice.

In October 1943, under conditions of great security, a special train arrived at Clunderwen station from London. It carried a mysterious group of high-ranking RAF and Army officers and included the famous inventor Barnes Wallis. At the station part of the train was detached, and the engine pulled one of the carriages northwards along the line towards Maenclochog. The train stopped about a mile south of the Maenclochog tunnel. Before long a Mosquito aircraft was heard by local farmers approaching the tunnel, and the aircraft followed its first run by making a number of other runs towards the tunnel entrance. Clearly there was some sort of bombing activity going on, although there were no explosions. Then the aircraft flew back to its base at RAF Angle. The secret party of military gentlemen returned to their train looking very satisfied, and then went back down the line towards Clunderwen, returning the same day to London.

After the War it became clear just how important this particular episode was in military history. The Mosquito aircraft was aiming and dropping prototype "bouncing bombs" invented by Barnes Wallis. The bombs were spherical, being made for the purposes of the test of wood clad with cast-iron. A number of the bombs were dropped on the approach to the tunnel. One or two hit the southern portals of the tunnel, causing considerable damage to the stonework. Others missed the tunnel completely, bouncing over the hill and landing in pieces in the field beyond. However at least one bomb bounced along the line and scored a direct hit, entering the tunnel, bouncing against the walls in the darkness and emerging at the other end as planned.

The military gentlemen were delighted with the success of this experiment, and Barnes Wallis was encouraged to continue with his development work. Eventually the bouncing bomb, further refined, was used in the famous Dam Busters Raid on the reservoirs of the Ruhr Valley in Germany. The raid was only partly successful, but the propaganda value of the exercise was enormous, providing a tremendous psychological lift for the people of Britain during the darkest days of the War.

Most of the traces of the Maenclochog Tunnel bombing exercise were removed by the Army shortly afterwards, but some remains of the dummy bouncing bombs have been found in the neighbourhood in recent years.

Date : 1943   *Source: Gale p 59*

3.12 The Duke of Edinburgh's Chair

Newgale is one of the most exposed places on the Pembrokeshire coast, and the great pebble beach is constantly changing its profile (and its position) in response to the action of tides and storm waves. Over the last hundred years or so the beach has been stabilised by the road and by the constant attentions of Council workmen, but during severe westerly storms accompanied by high tides the road is still blocked by pebbles; and flooding still occurs now and then in the valley of the Brandy Brook.

There have been at least three inns at Newgale, in more or less the position of the present Duke of Edinburgh inn. Every time an inn is destroyed, its successor is built a little further inland. Around 1800 there was an inn called "Sinnett's Hotel", some way to the west of the road and in a position now occupied by the sandy beach. Its pine end faced the sea, and it had a thatched roof; but it was used by many thousands of travellers and it was large enough to entertain the gentlemen of Pembrokeshire to sumptuous dinners during the Annual Newgale Races. It was destroyed by a great storm in 1859 which was responsible for the wrecking of over a hundred vessels around the coasts of Wales.

Sinnett's Hotel was later replaced by the Bridge Inn (located where the pebble bank now stands) kept by a Mrs Allen. This inn became famous in 1882 when it was visited by the Duke of Edinburgh on his way from Haverfordwest to St David's. He arrived in a landau pulled by four fine horses, and followed by his retinue. Mrs Allen laid on a sumptuous lunch for the royal party, and the chair on which the Duke sat while enjoying his meal was thereafter greatly treasured by the landlady. It became something of a tourist attraction, and was always pointed out to visitors as "The Duke of Edinburgh's chair". In honour of the royal visit, the inn was renamed The Duke of Edinburgh, and a royal coat of arms was placed over the door.

Sadly, a great disaster overtook the inn in 1895. During another terrible storm, the pebble bank was breached by the waves and the inn was completely destroyed. Mrs Allen and her daughter escaped after grabbing twenty gold sovereigns from the till, and managed to survive by clinging to some wooden railings in the position of the present Duke of Edinburgh Inn. Later they were rescued with great difficulty by some heroic neighbours. But as they hung on for dear life with the waves washing over them and the screaming of the wind in their ears, they watched the building disintegrate. The inn furniture floated by, driven up the flooded valley by the force of the storm. But, to her great grief, Mrs Allen never again saw the famous chair upon which the Duke of Edinburgh had placed his royal backside.

Date: 1896   *Source: Phillips p 44*

3.13 Good Hunting in Canaston Woods

One of the great estates of Pembrokeshire in the early part of the last century was the Slebech Estate, which comprised about 3,700 acres in the centre of the county. Much of the estate lay on the north shore of the Eastern Cleddau River, with a magnificent parkland of rolling countryside around Blackpool Quay and Slebech Hall itself. When the Baroness de Rutzen inherited the estate in 1830 she and the Baron moved to Slebech Hall and began to experience the responsibilities and pleasures of country life.

The Baron de Rutzen greatly valued the sporting rights on his land and on the adjoining river estuary, and fishing and wildfowling parties were organized for the pleasure of the local gentry. The Baron himself was an expert with both rod and gun. He embarked upon a careful breeding programme on the estate, importing blackfowl from Russia and greatly increasing the numbers of other game birds.

However, the Baron came originally from Hungary; and he was far from content with the mild entertainment provided by the shooting of game birds. So he decided to import assorted animals from the continent which would liven things up. Among these were wild boars, which had long been extinct in the United Kingdom. In November 1834 a cage containing two fearsome creatures arrived via Hamburg, following a deal with the Duke of Brunswick. The two wild boars, one male and the other female, were let loose in Canaston Woods. In the years that·followed they, and their numerous progeny, provided exciting sport for the Baron and his friends as they rushed about in the woods on horseback.

As one might expect, the Baron's tenants and his farming neighbours were anything but amused by this turn of events, for the boars frequently strayed out of the woodlands and did a great deal of damage to growing crops. In addition, many of the locals became too frightened to go out at night, fearing that the copses and thickets were populated by fearsome creatures which would attack them without warning. Hostility built up to such a pitch that at last the Baron was forced to agree to get rid of the wild boars. He promised to clear all of them from the woods not by a deliberate extermination campaign but by more intensive hunting. And so he enjoyed several more exciting years of hunting before the last of the animals was killed.

The locals complained that the boars "took an unconscionable time a-dying"; but they dared not complain too much since they knew that the Baron was also toying with the idea of importing European **wolves** into the Slebech estate woodlands.........

Date: c 1840   *Sources: Miles p 149, Morris 1948*

3.14 The Last Marros Fair

Many of the small towns and villages of West Wales used to have fairs of their own, many of them granted by charter during the Middle Ages. The dates of the fairs were jealously guarded, and the events were of great importance to the local community for the buying and selling of cattle, poultry and many other items produced by farmers, smallholders and cottagers. As the centuries passed there were many disputes about whether certain fairs were held legally or illegally, and villages and towns vied with each other in attempting to promote their own fairs and to destroy those held by competitors.

In days gone by there were two annual fairs at Marros, one held on Whit Monday and the other on 21st August. The fair would be held close to the village churchyard. Sheep, horses and other kinds of animals were bought and sold, as were many domestic items such as articles of clothing, cakes, vegetables and woollen fabrics. The local farmers always brewed beer for the fair, and this home-brew contributed greatly to the spirit of the occasion as well as earning a tidy income for the amateur brewers. However, around 1863 a law was passed which forbade farmers from selling their own ale at fairs. This caused great resentment, since local publicans could purchase licenses for sales of ale on the fair ground.

At last the dispute came to a head. In 1863, on the occasion of the August fair at Marros, the publicans asked the police to attend the fair in order to prevent the farmers from selling their home-made ale. The police duly enforced the law, which delighted the publicans but incensed the farmers. So the farmers took their revenge. The publicans were selling their beer in a house close to the churchyard. In the garden there happened to be two beehives, and a couple of the farmers contrived to creep into the garden unnoticed, where they tipped over both of the hives. Two huge swarms of bees, incensed at this intrusion into their privacy, swarmed out and angrily filled the whole house. There was pandemonium. Everyone in the house was forced to flee, and everyone was stung, some being quite seriously injured. The fair ended in total chaos, with the farmers having obtained their revenge.

No fair was ever held in Marros again. The episode with the bees discouraged the publicans, who were not keen to return to Marros, and the farming community refused to support any future fairs since they were now banned from selling their home-made ale. And so died another ancient West Wales tradition.

Date : c 1863   *Source: Curtis p 322*

3.15 Murder on the Maenclochog Railway

During the construction of the Maenclochog Railway in 1873-1876, there were various nationalities among the navvies. Many of them moved from one railway construction project to another; and the gangs or teams were close-knit and fiercely independent. The navvies worked hard and drank hard, and there were frequent brawls involving groups of Irishmen, Welshmen and Englishmen. As the railway snaked its slow and painful way across country a work camp would be established and used for weeks or months in a particular locality, bringing total disruption to the local community but also a great deal of local trade to shopkeepers and innkeepers. Then the camp would be moved to the next point along the line, and peace would return.

On the evening of October 13th 1874 the ill feeling between the Welsh and English navvies came to a head in a furious argument in The Cross Inn at Llanycefn. A feud had been developing for several months between George Jefferies and his cronies on the English side and Nathaniel Evans, Joseph Evans and John Williams on the Welsh side. The Welshmen were from the Maenclochog area, but they lived with the other workers in "the railway huts". After a pub brawl, the three Welshmen waylaid Jefferies in the dark lane leading back towards the huts. They beat him unconscious with heavy ash staves, and then dragged him across the river and left him at the side of the road. Then the culprits returned to their quarters. Later on, another navvy found Jefferies and took him to the huts, but he never regained consciousness. He died a few days later. The evidence appeared very strong against the three men, and they were arrested and charged with murder.

In due course the case came to be heard in the Shire Hall in Haverford-west. In the public gallery was Mrs Jefferies, the wife of the victim. The jury of respectable local men was sworn in, and the case commenced under the supervision of the Judge.

There was never any doubt in anybody's mind that the Evans brothers and John Williams had been responsible for the killing. There had been various witnesses to the fight if not the murder, but during their testimonies to the court these witnesses appeared to have forgotten a great deal of what transpired on the fateful night. The prosecuting barrister was confronted, in effect, with a "wall of silence" on the part of the railway navvies. The defending barrister put up a good case on behalf of the three accused, and called several well-known local farmers to give evidence as to their good character. There was general hilarity when Thomas Thomas Ty Mawr failed to come to the witness stand when called, but insisted on coming out of turn, after the next witness had been called.

In his summing up, the Judge pointed out to the jury that the killing of the Englishman had been the result of a drunken brawl, and explained that the jurors could consider the option of a manslaughter verdict as an alternative to a murder verdict. The jury was absent for a comparatively short time, and when the members returned there was a tense silence in the court-house. The Judge put the question: "Do you find the prisoners at the bar guilty or not guilty?" The foreman immediately replied "Not guilty!" The Judge was astonished, and leaned forward to address the foreman again. "Don't you find them guilty of anything?" he asked. "No!"

replied the foreman, decisively. The Judge sat back with a resigned look on his face. "I am glad, gentlemen," he said, "that that was your verdict and not mine." And with that he did his duty and released the three prisoners.

The decision of the jury was met with incredulity in Haverfordwest but with general approval in the Maenclochog area. The dead Englishman had obviously been an unpleasant sort of fellow. When all was said and done, the accused were stalwarts of the community, and the community had stood by them in their hour of need. So far as the locals were concerned, justice had been done.

Date: c 1880   *Source: Phillips p 86, Gale p 17*

Then the culprits returned to their quarters........

3.16 Visit from the King of Lundy

In the early 1600s a notorious pirate called Thomas Salkeld used Lundy
Island as the base for his piratical operations. He referred to himself as the
King of Lundy, and for a while his authority was unchallenged. There
were other kings of Lundy before and after Salkeld, but we have rather
more information about the dastardly deeds in which he was personally
involved. He and his pirate band were feared throughout the whole of the
Bristol Channel area, and occasionally they raided the Pembrokeshire
coast. In the year 1609 Salkeld entered Milford Haven. He sailed to the
village of Dale, where he robbed the people of their possessions, burnt
their houses, and took a sailing vessel from the quayside. He captured two
further vessels, one owned by George Escott of Bridgewater and another
owned by John Bennet of Appledore. Then he captured a sailing vessel
owned by William Young of Pembroke, which was setting off on a trading
voyage to Ireland. With his loot and his prisoners, and with his captured
ships, Salkeld landed on Lundy, raised his standard over the island and
declared himself King of Lundy. He then proclaimed that he wished that
he could have the heart of the King of England on the point of his sword.

Having taken over the island, Salkeld forced his prisoners to carry stones
for the construction of a new quay. Later a Flemish ship called at the
island, and Salkeld sent out a rowing-boat with an emissary who offered a
pilot. The captain suspected a plot and managed to escape, as did another
vessel from Weymouth on the same day. Somewhat disappointed by these
failures, Salkeld determined to strengthen his hold on the island. He
shaved the heads of his captives in token of their slavery, and set them to
work in building a fort and a platform on which he planned to mount his
cannon. He addressed his "slaves" as a ruler might address the meanest of
his subjects, informing them that he was now their sovereign and that any
who did not give their allegiance to him would be strung up on the
gallows.

The prisoners suffered day after day of unremitting toil. But they lived in
such appalling conditions that they could take it no longer, and plans were
hatched for a takeover of the island kingdom. One dark night an escape
plan was formulated, with George Escott elected as leader. Somehow he
had managed to obtain some weapons, and after the prisoners had
managed to make a hole in the back of their prison, he led an attack on
Salkeld's confederates while Salkeld himself was fast asleep. Some of the
pirates were captured and others fled. By popular acclaim Escott was now
appointed as commander of the slaves, and he declared that the island was
once again the property of the King of England. Seeing that all was lost,
Salkeld managed to take a boat out into the anchorage, where he boarded
Escott's own sailing ship and made good his escape. What happened after
that to the King of Lundy is not known, but it was with great relief that the
prisoners from Pembroke and the other home ports of the captured vessels
were able to return to the safety of the mainland.

Date 1609   *Source: Curtis p 11, p 65*

3.17 Horse Wedding in Cwm Cych

In Pembrokeshire it was once the custom in the country districts for "horse weddings" to take place. These may have originated in the violent Celtic horse rituals which were common up to about 2000 years ago; but the events were innocent enough during the last 200 years.

On the day of a wedding the bridegroom would ride to the house of his intended bride, with up to 40 of his friends and relatives also attending on horseback. He would hammer on the door of his beloved, finding it barred and bolted. The lady would appear at an upstairs window. Then the bridegroom would demand, often in elaborate verse, her immediate surrender. One of her relatives would then appear and refuse to giver her up. After some negotiation, it would be agreed that a friend of the groom could enter the house and fetch the bride. He would search high and low, and eventually find her. Then he would take her out through the back door, mount her behind him on a fresh horse, and gallop off into the distance. The groom, still being denied possession of the bride, would take up the chase, accompanied by all his friends. Sometimes these violent and noisy chases would go on for many miles, until both horses and riders were exhausted. Accidents were not unusual, and usually there was a mock battle before the bride was finally won by the groom and carried off to the church in triumph. In one tragic chase in South Pembrokeshire around the year 1800, a bride who was being hotly pursued by her intended husband waded her horse across a swollen river, only to be drowned.

Sometimes there were frantic horse races after the wedding ceremony as well. Bride, groom and guests would mount their steeds and gallop from the church to the house where the wedding celebration was to be held. There was always great admiration for the horse which reached the house first. A genial old squire who lived at Glaspant, near Capel Iwan, once sent three of his horses to a wedding in the village. After the wedding it was common knowledge that there would be a furious horse race from Capel Iwan to the bride's house in Cwm Cych. The squire's best horse was called Comet, and he fully expected it to win the race. The only problem was that it was a headstrong creature which paid little attention to the wishes of the rider; and since the horse race was due to pass the entrance to the Glaspant driveway the squire decided that Comet was quite liable to head for home instead of heading for the wedding reception. So he arranged for all his servants, both men and women, to station themselves at the road junction, armed with brooms, staves, walking sticks and shovels, simply to discourage Comet from heading for his stable.

At last, the wedding ceremony over, the horse riders came galloping into view, accompanied by much cheering and a thunder of hooves. Sure enough, Comet was in the lead. As the horse approached the road junction the squire gave a signal and the servants shouted and waved their sticks and brooms and beat their shovels on the ground, making as much noise as they could. Comet was successfully diverted along the road towards Cnwc-y-bettws, and in due course proved to be the hero of the day. It was said for months afterwards that the old squire was as proud of his horse as the young husband was of his new wife.

Date: c 1840   Sources: Davies p 35, Curtis p 208

3.18 The Forgers of St Clears

One day in the spring of 1816 a coach stopped at the White Lion Inn in St Clears. Out stepped a striking and elegantly dressed middle-aged woman. She could only walk with the aid of crutches, and she was helped into the inn by a young man who turned out to be her son. The coach party was accompanied by three people on horseback, two of whom were her nephews and the other her daughter, a young lady of extraordinary beauty. The members of the party were all well dressed, and from their bearing it was clear that they were aristocrats. The locals were keen to find out more about them. It turned out that the head of the family was Mrs Baines, and that the two nephews had the name of Thomson. Within a few days they took a lease on a small cottage called "White Cottage", just on the edge of the village.

The family settled in and visits were soon being exchanged with the members of the local gentry. The beautiful Miss Baines was the centre of attention, and she was declared to be a lady of remarkable talents, elegant accomplishments and fascinating manners. She and her cousins were soon absorbed into the social scene, attending parties, soirees and other events throughout the area. However it was frequently noted by their neighbours that the invalid Mrs Baines hardly ever left the cottage, while young Mr Baines appeared to be very shy and withdrawn. He spent a great deal of time in a small darkened room in the cottage, and his mother informed visitors that he was passionately fond of chemical experiments. The darkened room could only be entered through the living room, and when Mr Baines was not working there it was kept securely locked. The strange young man never went out in broad daylight, although he was sometimes spotted taking some exercise along the local lanes at dead of night.

The Baines family had strange eating habits. They ordered and paid for surprisingly large quantities of meat, vegetables and other groceries from the shopkeepers of St Clears; and sometimes their over-supply of provisions was such that they would offer a saddle of mutton, or a turkey, or a few loaves of bread to their nearest neighbours. The locals were also mystified by a strange event which occurred in the village during the summer. A notice appeared in the newspaper to the effect that a pocket-book containing a large sum of money in Bank of England notes and local bank notes had been found by one of the Thomson brothers in the vicinity of St Clears. The notice said that the pocket book could be reclaimed by the loser by application to Mr A Thomson of White Cottage. Apparently the only witness to the finding of the pocket-book was the local vicar, who saw the young man pick it up off the ground and examine the bank notes which it contained. Apparently no one ever reclaimed the pocket-book or the money, and the incident was soon forgotten.

At about the same time the local newspaper began to draw attention to the fact that an old established bank in Carmarthen was suffering as a consequence of expertly forged bank notes. The Bank of England was also suffering as a result of forgeries circulating in the Carmarthen area. One of the neighbours of the Baines family was a Mr Thomas, who ran a legal practice in the town. He had sharp eyes and a sharp intellect, and he indicated to one of the partners of the Carmarthen bank that he had certain suspicions concerning Mrs Baines and her son. The bank partner agreed to call on the Thomas family in St Clears, and a few days later the two men walked past White Cottage. The beautiful Miss Baines and one of her cousins were seated in the porch, and the two men approached them with a view to engaging them in conversation. They were surprised when there was a flurry of movement inside the cottage and by the alarm which they saw in the young lady's face.

Within a few days of this small incident it was rumoured that there had been a great deal of nocturnal activity in the garden of the cottage, and that the mysterious darkened room was now left open all the time. All of the equipment used by young Mr Baines for his "chemical experiments" had disappeared. Furthermore, the young man himself disappeared, and his mother explained that his pursuits had damaged his health, as a consequence of which he had travelled to Bath for medical advice. In November the rest of the family also left St Clears, travelling to meet the mail coach at Carmarthen. The young bloods of the neighbourhood were particularly sad to see the departure of the beautiful Miss Baines.

When the family arrived at Carmarthen they lodged in a local inn for the night, and Mrs Baines asked one of the waiters to go to the coach office in order to secure places on the morning coach to Bath. She gave the waiter a £10 note, which he duly presented in exchange for the tickets. Purely by chance one of the partners of the Carmarthen bank happened to be in the coach office at the time. He thought he noticed something unusual about the £10 note, examined it and found it to be a forgery. He made enquiries about Mrs Baines and her daughter, and found that both in St Clears and Carmarthen the family had made innumerable purchases from local tradesmen, always paying for their supplies with bank notes. At last the net was closing around the forgers, and the bank partner obtained a warrant for the arrest of the two ladies. They were duly apprehended while they were eating their dinner in the Carmarthen inn, and taken into custody. Messengers were sent after the son, who was supposedly in Bath; and he was eventually found in lodgings in Bristol, complete with all of the implements of his trade including plates, dies, paper and printers' inks. All five members of the Baines family were placed in prison.

It was many months before justice ran its course. The ladies were frequently visited in prison by admirers who were inevitably enchanted by their sparkling conversation and elegant manners. At last, in court, the case against the family was proved and all were sentenced to death. However, young Mr Baines promptly made a full and frank admission of his own guilt, and pleaded that the rest of the family were innocent. As a result of his testimony his two cousins were given a free pardon and the sentence on his mother and sister was commuted to one year's imprisonment. The two exotic ladies served their term in prison, although this appears not to have presented them with any great hardship, for their social life continued unabated under a very enlightened prison regime. Young Mr Baines hatched an escape plot, but was too incompetent to carry it through; and he was duly executed on the gallows in Carmarthen gaol. At the end of their year in prison the ladies left Carmarthen and moved to London. Mrs Baines threw away her crutches, which she no longer needed; and Miss Baines became a famous actress, and then a companion to a Countess in Florence, and finally married a noble lord.

Date : c 1820   *Source: Curtis p 230*

3.19 The Devil's Mischief in Lawrenny

Many years ago the good people of Lawrenny were moved to rebuild the semi-derelict church in their village so that they could give thanks to God in a proper manner. They met to discuss all the details of the design and building work, and decided that many tons of new stone were required.

At the time the great limestone quarries of West Williamston were in full swing on the other side of the Cresswell River, with occasional explosions disturbing the peace and quiet and clouds of white dust drifting across the landscape. The quarries produced limestone chippings for the Pembroke-shire lime kilns, and also blocks of hard whitish limestone for the dockyard at Pembroke Dock and for sale further afield. It was decided to purchase several cargoes of stone blocks from the quarries, and so a small coastal sailing barge was hired to transport the stone from West Williamston to the beach close to the village. This could only be done at high tide, since for much of the time the mud banks of the creek were high and dry above the water surface.

On the appointed day the barge took on its first load of limestone in one of the "docks" close to the quarries, crossed the river, and unloaded its cargo on the beach ready to be loaded into horse-drawn carts for the short journey to the church site. Night fell before all of the stone could be moved off the beach. At midnight the Devil came prowling along the shore and found the pile of stones. "Aha!" he said to himself. "Just what I need for making some stepping stones across the river, so that I can go and do my mischief in Upton and Cosheston!" So he threw all of the remaining stones into the sea, in the narrow channel at the mouth of the Carew-Cresswell river basin.

Next day another cargo of stones was delivered on the high tide, and once again the villagers failed to move all the stone before it got dark. Along came the Devil, and again he threw the rest of the stones into the middle of the channel. Now he was getting very satisfied that before long his stepping stones would be complete; but his smugness turned to fury when the locals decided that they had enough stone for the church restoration, and the shipments stopped. So the Devil's plans to do mischief in the parishes of Upton and Cosheston were thwarted.

At low tide you can still see the piles of stones on the river bed near the confluence of the Carew and Cresswell Rivers. (On the map they are called "Black Mixen", although the correct term is "Misken", an old Pembroke-shire word for a muck heap or midden.) If you are reluctant to believe that the Devil put the stones there, you might believe that they are piles of ballast dumped by the sailing vessels which came into the river to pick up cargoes of West Williamston stone. But that story is much less interesting than the one about the Devil, told to local children in the early years of the century......

Date: 1850   *Source : Mr David James*

3.20 The Pembroke Castle Dragon

In the early nineteenth century Pembroke Castle was in a ruinous state. However it was a perfect playground for small boys, who would explore among the battlements and cellars and piles of rubble, allowing their imaginations to run riot. Beneath the Castle there is a natural limestone cavern called "The Wogan", and over the centuries many attempts have been made to block its entrance from the riverside.

One day some local boys were walking along the river near the Castle. As they approached The Wogan they noticed that there was a small opening through the wall which blocked its mouth. The boys dared each other to go through the opening, fearing that they would find ghosts and monsters within. At last one or two of the lads plucked up the courage to creep into the cave. They had a small dog with them, and the dog went through the opening first. The dog sensed that there was something inside, and the boys heard it growl as they peered into the darkness. At first the boys could hear nothing but the regular drip, drip, drip of water from the cave roof onto the slimy floor. Then they heard a sound that was difficult to describe, as if something heavy was dragging itself along the floor of the cave. As their eyes became accustomed to the darkness they saw a long snout with rows of gleaming white teeth. With horror they saw the jaws snap shut and then open again.

Quite convinced that they were being chased by a dragon, the boys screamed and fled. As they scrambled out through the narrow opening their poor dog was left behind, and just as it emerged into the daylight they saw the terrible jaws close over one of its back legs. The dog managed to scramble away from the cave but was very badly injured, and it died soon afterwards. Even more frightened and now quite convinced that what they had seen was real rather than imagined, the boys ran to the Castle watchman and described the creature to him as best they could. They said that it was huge, with bright eyes and a scaly body and short legs with big claws on its feet.

The boys were so clearly in a state of shock that the watchman had to take their story seriously, especially when he saw the mutilated body of the little dog. He gathered a dozen men together, and after they had armed themselves to the teeth they went off to The Wogan to fight the dragon. They entered the cave with torches, and sure enough they found the monster in the corner. After a frantic battle they managed to kill it, and its body was then taken away and burnt in tar down by the shore.

The Dragon of The Wogan turned out not to be a gigantic dragon at all, but really a rather small and pathetic crocodile. No one could say where it had come from, but we can speculate that it was brought ashore by a sailor from one of the trading vessels anchored at Pembroke Quay, just below the Castle. Probably the crocodile had grown to such a size that the sailor could no longer look after it. He had dumped it in The Wogan, where the poor creature was almost starved to death until a small dog provided it with an opportunity of grabbing a decent meal.

Date : c 1810   *Source : Mr Patrick James*

3.21 The Cornish Smugglers

There is a very long tradition of smuggling in Pembrokeshire, since the complicated coastline is almost impossible for constables and excise men to patrol effectively. The goods which have been brought in to small isolated coves by mysterious vessels, often at dead of night, have varied according to the laws and taxes of the day. At various times between the 1500s and the present day, salt, sugar, wine, tobacco and drugs have all figured prominently in the smuggling trade.

One of the popular areas for smuggling was the coast around Amroth, Marros and Pendine; illegal goods could easily be transported from this area into Pembrokeshire and to the town of Carmarthen, where there was a ready market and a growing population. Around the year 1810 a dozen Cornish men arrived in the Marros and Pendine area. They were described as "remarkably fine men, powerful beyond usual". They were professional smugglers and in order to increase the effectiveness of their trade they dispersed to Haverfordwest, Tenby, Pembroke, Manorbier and Llanstephan. Two of the men, named Truescot and Dickdelly, lived in the old farmhouse at Napps, near Pendine. Occasionally ships would come in to Gilman Point, where they would unload cargoes of wine and spirits. The contraband goods were first of all stored in a large cave called Gilman Church, and when the smugglers were sure that there were no excise men in the vicinity they would move the alcohol to the cellars of the farmhouse. They had a hidden cellar which could be entered only by a trap-door from the room above. This trap-door was concealed by a large wooden box filled with soil and flowering plants. Although the excise men were suspicious of the men's activities and visited Napps Farm frequently, they never found the cellar and could never find any evidence of smuggling.

One of the smugglers, whose name was Armstrong, was once stopped by the excise officers as he was approaching Carmarthen town with a horse and cart. The cart was full of smuggled wine and spirits. There is no record of how he managed to deceive the officers, but apparently he escaped by using a combination of tact and enormous strength. On another occasion Armstrong escaped from seven excise officers who were trying to arrest him.

The smuggling ring was never broken up, and Truescot survived to a ripe old age, dying in the town of Pembroke around 1865. His daughter kept an inn in the town, and another daughter kept one in Haverfordwest. Both of them ran very successful enterprises, probably because they acquired their wine and spirits at very good prices via certain interesting and irregular distribution networks.

Date : c. 1810   *Source: Curtis p 264*

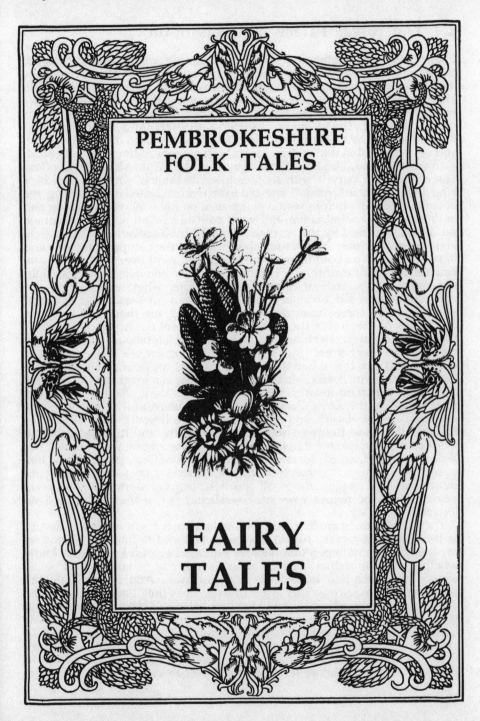

PEMBROKESHIRE
FOLK TALES

FAIRY
TALES

4.1 The Royal Palace on Grassholm

In one of the famous stories of **The Mabinogion** there is a particularly blood-thirsty episode in which the heroic fighting men of Britain avenge the insults suffered by Branwen the daughter of Llyr at the hands of the Irish. The old tale relates that in a series of ferocious battles in Ireland the Irish were defeated but only seven of the British heroes survived to return home. Among these were Taliesin, Pryderi and Manawyddan. Bendigeidfran, the chief of the British, was fatally injured during the battle, and he commanded that instead of dying in agony he should be beheaded.

"Take my head," he said, "and carry it to the White Mount in London. There you must bury it with its face towards France. And you will be a long time upon the road." The old warrior concluded by detailing the delights which the heroes would experience on the way, with feasting and birds singing, and relaxation and good company. And so the seven men set off accompanied by the severed head and by Branwen the daughter of Llyr. Soon after they had started their journey they stopped to rest, and Branwen looked on both Ireland and Wales and wept over the tragedy that had befallen both countries because of her. And she heaved a great sigh, and broke her heart. Her colleagues buried her where she died.

The men travelled on and spent seven years in feasting at Harlech, entertained by three magical birds which sang for them the songs of Rhiannon. At the end of the seventh year they set out across the sea and travelled to Gwales, which was the old name for Grassholm. On the island they found a magnificent royal palace overlooking the sea. They went in to the hall, and saw that it had three doors. Two of the doors were open, but the third was kept closed. Manawyddan, who was a magician, warned his colleagues that they must never open the third door. And so the seven men stayed in the Royal Palace in joyful and delightful company. Their sufferings in Ireland, and their sorrows following the deaths of Bendigeidfran and Branwen were quite forgotten, and it seemed that all memories of unpleasant things had been removed from their minds. The Wondrous Head, which remained in excellent condition, proved to be fine company for the seven men, telling them ancient tales and singing innumerable jolly songs. As in all the best magical stories, eighty years passed while the heroes were on Grassholm; but to them it seemed no longer than a day.

Then one of the company, who was called Heilyn son of Gwyn, looked at the closed door in the hall of the Palace and said to himself "Shame on my beard if I do not open that door. For unless I open it I will never know whether the things that are said about it are true or false." And so he opened the door and looked towards Cornwall. And immediately the seven men became conscious again of every loss they had ever sustained and of every kinsman and friend that had fallen in battle, and of every ill thing that had afflicted them. They felt even more keenly the loss of their Lord Bendigeidfran, and remembered again the instruction that he had given them many years ago to take his Wondrous Head to London. From that moment on they could not rest, and so they set off across the sea to Pembrokeshire and thence to London in order to complete their mission.

Date : c 800 AD   *Source : Jones & Jones p 39*

4.2 The Mountain Dwarfs of Presely

The Presely Hills (or Mountains, as we should properly call them) dominate the landscape of Pembrokeshire. The summits are often shrouded in mist, and the first and last snows of winter blanket the high slopes. There are wide expanses of moorland, and rocky crags echoing with the cries of ravens. In the old days, when the English-speaking people of South Pembrokeshire hardly ever travelled north of the Landsker, Mynydd Presely was a place of mystery and rumour, seen from afar and largely unknown.

Not surprisingly, the people of South Pembrokeshire had some strange notions about Presely. This was the domain of giants and dragons, and the place where great treasures were hidden in the rocky ground. It was also the domain of dwarfs and hobgoblins, who lived in caves and who shunned all contact with human beings.

An old story from Narberth explains the origin of the Presely dwarfs. Once upon a time St Peter sent three white and perfect souls from Paradise to be brought into the world as newborn babies. However, on their way into the world of human beings they were met by the Devil, who spat on all three of them. They had to stop and cleanse themselves in a crystal stream up in the hills; and because of this delay they reached their destination ten minutes late. Their bodies never grew to a proper size, and they remained as very small children. By chance the three of them met some years later, and they recognized that they were oddities with much in common. They could not face the ridicule of other children, and so they ran away to Mynydd Presely. There they lived a secret life in caves under the ground, and they became the first dwarfs. Only on very rare occasions were they seen by normal human beings.......

Another old Pembrokeshire tale recounts that at the time of Noah's Flood there were seven poor persons, too wicked to be taken on board the Ark and too good to be drowned. And so as the waters rose they clung to the sides of the huge wooden vessel as it floated away. As the floods abated the summit of Presely, called Foel Cwmcerwyn, appeared above the surface just as the Ark was floating by. The seven poor people, who by now were tired and hungry, jumped off the Ark and scrambled ashore. They made their home in the hills, becoming dwarfs and hiding away from all further contact with the descendants of Noah.

Date: c 1700?   *Source : T. Gwynn Jones p 82*

4.3 The Ancients

The Eagle, who was the King of the Birds, was feeling miserable. He sat on a narrow ledge on the great limestone cliff of Stackpole Head and wailed "Where will I get me a wife?" He looked far out to sea where he saw a dolphin playing in the waves. But he was in no mood to talk to the dolphin, so he spoke to the wind instead as it blustered and beat at the cliff face around him. "Alack and alas!" he cried. "My mate has died and who is worthy to replace her? I am the King of the Birds and I must have a wife."

"Marry the owl," said the South-West Wind. "Marry the owl who lives in the woods in the valley of the Taf." The Eagle blinked his eyes and said to himself "The South-West Wind advises me well. But one must not be hasty about such things. In view of my status I must make some careful enquiries about the owl. Is she worthy to be my Queen? Is she old and is she good?"

The South-West Wind knew the Eagle's thoughts but did not stay to converse further. Instead it sped away towards Mynydd Presely, bearing rain clouds and bringing rain to the parched lands. So the Eagle said to himself "I will go to the Bishop's lands of Menevia and ask my friend the Deer all about the Owl of the Taf."

The Eagle soared high into the sky and winged his way across St Bride's Bay to the land of St David. There he found his friend the Deer and summoned him to a woodland grove where they could speak in confidence. "Tell me, old friend," he said. "What do you know about Mistress Owl who lives in the valley of the Taf?" The Deer rubbed his antlers against the bark of an old Welsh oak tree. "Do you see this old oak tree, my friend?" he asked. "I am so old that I can remember this oak tree when it was only an acorn on the older oak tree across the way. It has taken fourteen hundred years for this oak to grow into a great tree. For seven hundred years it grew to its full glory. For another seven hundred years it has been dying. So old is it, King of the Birds, that I advise you to ask the old oak the age of Mistress Owl of the Taf."

The Eagle turned to the ancient oak tree and asked the question. Then the tree replied "O King, I have known Mistress Owl for many hundreds of years, so many hundreds that I have lost count of them. Mistress Owl was old when first I knew her. It is true that I am old, but my friend the Salmon of Roch is older than I. He may be able to help you. Go Sir, and ask him the age of Mistress Owl."

So the King of the Birds flew to the jagged carn at Roch, and there he found in the valley below a sunny pool in which basked a huge salmon. In reply to the Eagle's question the salmon said "Do not be impatient, young King. The Blackbird of Rudbaxton is older than I. He will know the age of Mistress Owl. Go and ask him."

The Blackbird of Rudbaxton was singing his heart out on the topmost branch of an ash tree when he saw the Eagle approach. At once he hid in the shadow of a tall rock, fearing that he was going to become the Eagle's supper. But the Eagle called out "Have no fear, happy blackbird. I mean you no harm. I come only to ask the age of Mistress Owl of the Taf." At this, the Blackbird ruffled his feathers and forgot his nervousness. "O mighty King," he said. "Do you see this old rock that casts its shadow on

the land? I can remember it when it was far far higher. In my childhood it was a rugged mountain. Each night before I go to rest I rub my beak upon it. Thus has the towering mountain been worn away to become a single rock. You know then that I am old, but even I cannot remember Mistress Owl any younger than she is today."

Now the Eagle became depressed, and feared that he would never discover the age of Mistress Owl. The Blackbird felt sorry for him. "Do not worry, O King," he said. I have a friend who is far older than I. If you will fly to the Toad of Freystrop, he may be able to tell you something about Mistress Owl." The Eagle gave his thanks. Then, spreading his mighty wings, he took off and flew south to Freystrop by the side of the Cleddau River. From a great height he saw the Toad resting in a muddy pool. When he descended he assured the Toad that he had no wish to eat him, but simply to ask him a question. On hearing the question the Toad hopped onto a tuft of moss and answered the King of the Birds. "Sir, I am an eater of dust," he said. "Yet I can never eat enough to satisfy my hunger. Around my pool and my bog you see the rolling hills of Daugleddau, and far to the north are the mountains of Presely. I can remember a time when this land was a great plain. I am old, very old. You can reckon my age when I tell you that it is I who have eaten away the land, making the valleys and hollows between the hills. Yet, old as I am, I can only remember Mistress Owl as a very old owl, hooting in the darkness just as she does today."

The Eagle thanked the Toad. Then, greatly relieved, he flew straight away to the Taf valley to find Mistress Owl. At last he was satisfied that she came from a good family, and that she was sufficiently old to be respectable. And so the King of the Birds and the Ancient Owl were married. The wedding guests were the Deer of Menevia, the Salmon of Roch, the Blackbird of Rudbaxton and the Toad of Freystrop, all of whom were very old. And as they celebrated the South-West Wind whistled by on its way to the mountains.

Date: c 1100 AD   *Source: E. Jones p 28*

4.4 The Legend of Skomar Oddy

Skomar Oddy is a gentle giant who sleeps in a great cave in the mountain beneath Presely Top or Foelcwmcerwyn. He sleeps so soundly that it is almost impossible to wake him, but once every hundred years he emerges to do some mighty deed before going off to sleep again. He is reputed to be none too bright, but very willing.

Once upon a time there were two sea monsters living in the deep waters off the coast of Pembrokeshire, near the mouth of Milford Haven. They were not on the best of terms, and one day they started to fight. So furious and ferocious was the battle that storm waves were created, crashing on the western cliffs and even affecting the shores of the Haven. The waves rolled up the waterway as far as Haverfordwest and Canaston Bridge. The sea surface was whipped up into a frenzy of white foam and flying spray. Many ships were sunk, and the huge waves damaged many cottages and other buildings close to the shore. Never had the locals seen such a storm.

As the sea monsters continued with their battle all the mud on the bottom of the sea was stirred up, and much of it was thrown into Milford Haven. Soon there was so much mud that the waterway began to disappear, with black slimy mud-banks taking the place of the wide expanses of clear deep water. The sea sprites, mermaids and other creatures which inhabited the waters became seriously worried. "What on earth shall we do?" they wailed. "Our homes are lost for ever, and all because of those stupid sea monsters!" But just as they were all giving up hope, one of the sea sprites had the bright idea of asking Skomar Oddy to come and help. "But he's fast asleep," said another, "And he won't wake up until the appointed time, when one hundred years is up." But they knew that Skomar Oddy was their only hope, and so they sent a deputation to Presely Top to meet him.

There, on the top of the mountain, they met some of the dwarfs and fairies who lived in those parts, and they explained their quest. They agreed to help, and they knew how to get into Skomar Oddy's cave. So down they went, into the bowels of the earth, until they came to a gigantic cavern; and there, fast asleep and snoring so loud that the sea sprites thought that they were in the middle of an earthquake, they found the gentle giant. They crawled all over him and kicked and pinched him and shouted in his ear, and at last he stirred and woke up. As he rubbed his eyes and yawned they explained their desperate plight, and at last he agreed to help, just so that he could get a bit of peace and quiet and go back to sleep again.

So Skomar Oddy emerged from his cave, with the sea sprites and the dwarfs and fairies in his pockets and hanging onto his coat, and with mighty three-mile strides he walked down to Milford Haven, with the countryside shaking as he went by. When he reached the mud-filled Haven he placed all the little people down on the shore and set to work, with one huge foot placed on the south shore and the other on the north shore. Thus straddling the Haven, he scooped out the mud in giant handfuls, flinging it aside onto the dry land. Then he moved down the Haven, placing his feet in new positions and scooping out more handfuls of mud as he went. At last he reached the outer part of the waterway and scooped out the last handfuls of mud. And just as he reached the open sea, one of the sea monsters overcame the other and killed it, causing the fury of the sea to subside. The sea sprites and the mermaids and the dwarfs and the fairies all cheered, for they knew that the clear deep blue waters of Milford Haven were safe.

Now that his job was well done, Skomar Oddy decided to return to his cave, and not forgetting to pick up the Presely dwarfs and fairies who had accompanied him, he took his leave. With the thanks of the sea sprites ringing in his ears he made his noisy and ponderous way back to Presely Top. There he set down his friends, re-entered his cave, and settled down into a deep and well-deserved sleep, hoping that he would be able to enjoy a hundred years in peace and quiet.

To this day visitors to Milford Haven can see the traces of Skomar Oddy's mighty work. On the south side of the Haven, where the rocks were soft, his feet sank into the shore as he worked. So the giant's footprints can be seen in the bays and creeks from Lawrenny to Angle. The biggest footprint of all is Angle Bay, which is almost two miles from heel to toe. The mud which Skomar Oddy threw out of the Haven landed on the countryside round about, and made the soils so fertile that the area became one of the richest farming districts in the whole of Wales.

The legend of Skomar Oddy is almost forgotten now, but at the end of the last century the children of Milford Haven all knew a little rhyme, which went like this:

"Skomar Oddy, Skomar Oddy,
No Head and all Body."

Perhaps one day the giant will emerge again from his slumbers, when he is needed by the people of Pembrokeshire to save them from some terrible catastrophe.

Date: 1750?   *Source: Rogers Rees p 76*

4.5 The Flying Boatman of Milford

One calm and moonlit night, long ago, a Milford fisherman set out in his skiff to do some fishing in the Haven. He took a bottle of whiskey to keep him warm, and told his wife that he would be back by the morning. However, he did not return until two days later; and when she remonstrated with him furiously, he explained that a very strange thing had happened to him out on the water. Apparently, he was quietly drifting along with his nets around midnight. Suddenly he was swept along in a great surge of water, and he realised that he was being carried along in a giant handful of water scooped up by Skomar Oddy. Before he could do anything about it he was flying through the air with the torrent of water, to land with a splash far out to sea. Luckily the sea was calm and he was a strong swimmer, and he struck out for his boat, which he could see still afloat some distance off. He reached the boat, managed to make it shipshape after the battering it had received from the giant, and made for the nearest land. This turned out to be a large island on the south side of St Bride's Bay. He was very tired as he scrambled ashore, but he was confronted by a group of hostile islanders. He pretended to be a half-wit, and in any case he did not speak their language, and in reply to their incomprehensible questions he simply repeated "Skomar, Skomar" in order to indicate that it was the giant's fault that he was in their midst. At last they decided he was no threat to them, and they let him go; and next day he managed to sail back to Milford. When he arrived home he found that his wife did not believe a word of his story; but it was a good story, and he stuck to it. The story became so well known among the fisher-folk of Milford that whenever, thereafter, a local fisherman was lost or delayed by the stormy waters around the coast it was said that he had been "got by Skomar Oddy".

Date: c 1800   *Source: Rogers Rees p 77*

........he was quietly drifting along with his nets around midnight.

The widow began to experience all sorts of problems, which eventually brought her and her seven children to the brink of starvation.

4.6 Fairy Tale from Canaston Woods

Once upon a time a poor woman was possessed by a devil, and she placed a curse upon her very own widowed sister who had offended her. The widow began to experience all sorts of problems, which eventually brought her and her seven children to the brink of starvation. Then, to complete the spell, the wicked sister gathered whatever eggshells she could find, filled them with dew, and fastened them up. She placed them in a thorn bush at the side of a path which she knew her sister would use. Along came the starving mother, desperately hunting for food, and when she found the eggs she uttered a cry of joy. She called her children, and together they made holes in the shells and sucked out the contents.

However, having drunk the dew they began to shrink in size and to fade away, and they would have vanished completely had not Jesus come along the path just then. He saw what was happening, and also saw the demon in the wicked sister. At once he commanded the demon to come out of her, and it fled at the sound of his voice. At the same moment the fading and shrinking of the mother and her seven children stopped; but now, being small and almost invisible they knew that they could no longer inhabit the world of human beings. So they fled away to the wilderness, to become the first fairies.

The people in the farms and cottages around Canaston Woods all knew this story, and to prevent such a thing happening again they always made sure that they broke up their eggshells into very small pieces before throwing them away.

Date: 1897   *Source: Rogers Rees p 15*

4.7 Protheroe and the Devil

In the early part of this century the fishermen of Marloes and Martin's Haven told many stories about the strength and prowess of a mysterious figure called Protheroe. He was apparently a giant who lived on Skomer Island, and it is quite possible that the tale of Skomar Oddy (Story 4.4) is derived from the same legend.

Once upon a time when St David returned to Pembrokeshire to convert the heathen and establish his monastery, he found that the Devil was in possession. The Saint ordered the Devil to leave the territory since it was now claimed for God. Upon this the Devil, in a fury, mounted a coal-black steed and leapt across St Bride's Bay from Menevia to Skomer Island. He landed on the cliff above Protheroe's Dock, where the hoof marks of the horse may still be seen imprinted in the rock. Protheroe, the strong man of Skomer, was living on the island at the time, and was somewhat alarmed by the arrival of the Devil. But he was a tolerant fellow, and for a while they got on well together.

Unfortunately, after observing Protheroe at work on the island, the Devil became jealous of his great strength and challenged him to a duel. Protheroe was at first reluctant, but at last agreed to a duel which would take the form of a game of quoits. The target was St Ann's Head, in the distance and across the sea. The loser in the quoits match would be required to leave the island. So Protheroe and the devil cast their quoits across the sea, and the strong man won the match. Great was the anger of the Devil, but he had to keep his side of the bargain and leave the island. Nobody knows where he went. And to this day there is a large white slab of rock near the base of the cliffs at St Ann's Head, not far from the site of the lighthouse, which is known as "Protheroe's Quoit".

Date : c 1900   *Source: Howells p 132*

4.8 Fairy Gift at Bangeston

At Bangeston, near Cosheston, there is a fine old house which was once inhabited by a gentleman well known in the Pembroke area. His wife had died, and he had no children, but a servant girl called Daisy looked after him and did the housework. On three successive nights Daisy was frightened out of her wits by a little man standing outside her bedroom window on the window-sill. He tapped earnestly on the glass, as if he was trying to get in. He was so small that Daisy knew he was a fairy. He had a white beard so long that it was tied several times around his waist.

At last the girl was so frightened that she asked her master if she might leave his service; but she was a good servant and he was reluctant to lose her, so he questioned her closely as to her reasons. At last she told him about the fairy on the window-sill. He promised that he would keep watch outside with a loaded musket, and said that he would shoot the intruder; but although the little man came again on the following nights nobody but Daisy ever saw him. Eventually, on the advice of her master, Daisy resolved to speak to the fairy. Next night he appeared again, and Daisy asked him what he wanted. He was so pleased to have established contact at last that he jumped up and down on the window-sill, smiled a toothy smile, and blew her a kiss. Then he beckoned her to follow him. She got up and dressed, went downstairs, opened the front door and walked into the yard. The little man was there, and he beckoned her to follow him into the copse alongside the lane. This she did.

Then she stopped at a special spot, took out a silver mattock from under his cloak, and gave it to her. He told her to start digging, and she was surprised that his voice was like the hum of a bee in a foxglove flower. She dug down exactly a yard and then came upon a bed of gold and silver coins. The fairy looked delighted. "You have got the treasure," he said. "But before you touch it, let me give you my charge. The first seven gold coins that you touch you must put safely by, and you must keep them for ever. So long as you do this, both you and yours, and your descendants, will have all the money you need. If you lose or spend these seven coins, your good luck will depart from you for ever. So beware!"

Having spoken thus, the little man disappeared in a blue flame and was never seen again. Daisy was now very rich. Eventually she married her master. The seven gold coins are still in possession of the family, and it continues to enjoy good fortune to this day.

Date: 1803　　　　　　　　　　　　　　　　*Source: Meredith Morris p 44*

4.9 The Fairies at Pendine

According to all accounts, fairies were not very common in the English-speaking parts of Pembrokeshire. However, the author Mary Curtis came across a number of stories about fairies in the area of Pendine, Marros and Laugharne. Since the Welsh language was still in quite common use during the 1800s in this area, it is quite possible that Celtic fairy traditions survived longer than they did in the heartland of Little England Beyond Wales.

It was said that in a field at Pantread, in Eglwyscummin parish, fairies were commonly seen dancing within a number of quite large fairy rings. The local people firmly believed that if you placed your foot within one of these circles you would be taken away by the fairies or forced to dance with them until someone came to rescue you. In the same area the fairies or *Tylwyth Teg* were sometimes seen by elderly people walking along the Pendine road.

There is a tradition that the fairies frequently visited Pendine village. On one occasion they attended divine service in the church, and the other members of the congregation were very impressed how well they behaved. Many years afterwards it was recounted that before the fairies entered the church they hung their cloaks on a sunbeam, for they had become wet during a shower of rain. Pendine people believed that these fairies lived in a field behind the Great House, for frequent fairy rings were to be seen there.

Date : c 1850

Source : Curtis p 297 & 321

Before the fairies entered the church they hung their cloaks on a sunbeam, for they had become wet during a shower of rain.

4.10 Mischief at Puncheston

Once upon a time, not very long ago, a well-known farmer who lived near Puncheston was taken to Withybush Hospital by ambulance suffering from a broken leg. He had clearly suffered a nasty accident while working on his farm. However the circumstances were somewhat mysterious, and caused the staff of the casualty department great difficulty when they came to make their case notes. The explanation given to them by the injured farmer was roughly as follows.

The farm where the accident occurred was well-known to local people, not only because of the eccentricities of the farmer himself, but because it was also reputed to be populated by the *Tylwyth Teg* or little people. While he was being treated by the doctor, the farmer explained that he had been painting his house. The time came to paint the drainpipes and gutters, and he placed his step-ladder up against the wall so that he could reach the gutter high above his front door. He climbed to the top of the ladder with his paint can and brush, and started work with great gusto. "And do you know," he said, with his voice full of indignation, "While I was up there I heard them little buggers laughing and giggling down below. And before I knew what was happening they pulled away the ladder right from under me. And down I went with a mighty crash. And here I am. And all the fault of them little buggers. Dammo, there's no knowing what they'll be up to next."

We do not know what the consultant surgeon entered on his record as the cause of this most unfortunate accident.

Date : c 1980　　　　　　　　　　　　　　　　　　*Source : word of mouth*

4.11 The Bitch of Aberdaugleddau

With the help of a most marvellous team of helpers, King Arthur was on a Quest. He had promised his young nephew Culhwch that he would help him to obtain the hand of the Princess Olwen in marriage. However, Olwen's father was unfortunately a wicked Irish giant called Yspaddaden Penkawr, and he set Arthur no less than forty impossible tasks to fulfill before he would even consider the matter further. Arthur was not a man to be put off by impossible tasks, for he had magical resources at his disposal, including wonderful magicians and good contacts in the Otherworld.

After consulting the Owl of Cwm Cawlwyd and the Eagle of Gwernabwy, Arthur found Mabon son of Modron in prison, and rescued him after a mighty battle. Then he asked his messengers "Which of the marvels should I now seek?" They replied that it was best to seek the two whelps of the bitch Rhymni, magical creatures whose whereabouts were unknown. So Arthur sent out messengers to make enquiries. When they returned Arthur asked "Now, is it known where she is?" One of them replied that the bitch and the whelps were at Aber Deu Gleddyf, which was the old name for Milford Haven. So Arthur and some of his helpers travelled to Milford, and there they visited the house of a man called Tringad. Arthur asked him "Have you heard of the bitch Rhymni and her whelps in these parts?" And knowing that all magical animals change form frequently in order to confuse mere mortals, the King added "In what shape is the bitch?" The poor man replied that Rhymni was indeed in the area, and that she went about in the shape of a huge she-wolf with her two whelps. He poured out his troubles to Arthur, saying that the magic hound had often slain his livestock, and that it lived lower down the Haven in a cave.

So Tringad told Arthur how to find the cave, and he embarked on his magical ship **Prydwen** in order to make an approach from the sea. He sent other men to hunt for the creatures by land, and to cut off their escape. They surrounded the cave, and when Arthur attacked from the sea he was able, no doubt by means of magic, to capture all three snarling wolves alive. Then they were miraculously changed back into normal hunting hounds, and Arthur took them with him as he set off on the next part of his Quest. Having completed the hunt for Rhymni and the whelps, Arthur's host dispersed, one by one, two by two.

Date: c 1050?   *Source: Jones & Jones p 126*

PEMBROKESHIRE
FOLK TALES

WITCHCRAFT
AND
MAGIC

5.1 John Jenkin the Conjuror

There are a number of strange stories connected with Nevern, some of them relating to magic and the occult. For example, it is believed that John Jenkin (Ioan Siengcyn), who was the schoolmaster in Nevern around 1780, was not only a poet but also a conjuror or *Consuriwr* who could summon up evil spirits. The story entitled "John Jenkin and the Evil Spirits" in the first volume of **Pembrokeshire Folk Tales** probably took place in Nevern.

John was the son of a Cardigan shoemaker, and was known locally as Shion Crydd Bach (John Little Cobbler); he is thought to have lived at Cwmgloyne, and for some years he was involved in the great educational movement started by the Rev Griffith Jones and centred upon the idea of the "circulating school." He died in 1796 at the ripe old age of 80. He left behind a number of elegies and other poems, but unfortunately no other stories of his occult powers have survived.

It may be that his reputation for dabbling in the occult had something to do with his poetic genius. We know that he was commissioned to write poems to commemorate great local events; and around the year 1790 he wrote a famous poem to celebrate the launching of the 50-ton schooner **Hawk**, built at Newport for Squire Lloyd of Cwmgloyne. In the poem he asked for a blessing on the new ship:

> Your wings playing high as the clouds,
> Your breasts cleaving the salt billows,
> Let your beak pierce the waves, your belly furrow them,
> Your rudder scatter them in spray-suds.

In the popular mind, if it was possible for John Jenkin to ask for a blessing on a new ship, was it not also possible for him to ask for a curse? It was well known that some of the "knowing ones" of Pembrokeshire, such as the Cunning Man of Pentregethin (see Tale 5.1 in **The Last Dragon**) could sell foul winds or fair, and could indeed cause ships on the high seas to encounter trouble or even to run upon the rocks. And from other tales circulating about John Jenkin, it was known that he was in close touch with the devil......

Date: 1790   *Source: Miles 1983, p 118*

5.2 Nasty Noise at Caerfarchell

Until quite recent times Pembrokeshire people have sustained primitive beliefs which may well be more than two thousand years old, dating from the shadowy pre-Christian world of Celtic tribalism. Some of these beliefs involve an element of superstition or even magic.

Under the floors of many old Pembrokeshire cottages there are horse's skulls. When Mr Thomas of Jordanston was replacing the floor of his old house in 1901 he discovered no less than 20 skulls; he claimed that they were there to ensure good acoustics, and he carefully replaced them beneath the new floor. When the first Calvinistic Methodist Chapel was built in Caerfarchell, near St David's, in 1763, the acoustics were found to be quite unsatisfactory. When the congregation had suffered from 64 years of terrible echoes and reverberations, they decided to rebuild the chapel; and one William Lewis, a faithful chapel-goer who was a seaman by profession, was given the task of sorting out the noise problem. So when the new foundations were being put in William promised to provide two horse's skulls, which he guaranteed would sort out the trouble. For good measure he provided four skulls, and one was placed under each of the four corners of the building. Sure enough, when the new chapel was inaugurated, the congregation found that the acoustics were magnificent. The Calvinistic Methodists were in principle fiercely opposed to all kinds of superstition, and it is interesting that they clearly considered the placing of the horse skulls under the foundations to be simply a matter of good building practice.......

Date: c 1837   *Sources: Jones p xxvii, James p 107*

5.3 The Wise Man of Templeton

In many Pembrokeshire communities there are still men and women who have a reputation for healing. Some of them are reputed to have special powers just like the magicians or wise men of past centuries.

About twenty years ago two cousins from the Haverfordwest area suffered from severe eczema on their forearms. This was a complaint that ran in the family. One of the cousins had a fine academic career and is still a well known teacher in the county. The other is a local farmer. For many years both men sought medical advice and tried various remedies in order to find a cure to their ailment. At long last the farmer was advised to consult the Wise Man of Templeton. We do not know the details, but the Wise Man used a secret charm, and the eczema was healed.

The Wise Man said he could heal the teacher as well, if only he would come and pay him a visit. The farmer immediately rang up his cousin and advised him to go to Templeton to see the old healer. However, the teacher's education, and the scepticism that went with it, would not permit him to visit someone whom he considered to be a "quack doctor". To this day the farmer has had no recurrence of the eczema, whereas the academic continues to suffer from the affliction.

Date: c 1970   *Source: Mr Patrick James*

5.4 Thieving at Cartlett Mill

In the last century Cartlett was the main "industrial area" of Haverfordwest. Here, by the riverside in more or less the position now occupied by the District Council offices, there were a number of industries including a saw mill and timber yard, a corn mill, a furniture factory, and depots for the import of coal and culm for local fireplaces and limestone to feed the Cartlett lime kilns. Not far away there was a pop-works and a brick-works. The river trade involving barges and sailing vessels was of vital importance for all of these businesses. In the old days power to drive the cogs of industry came from the Scotchwells leat, which carried water from Cartlett Brook to a water wheel on the site of the present Green's Garage.

Cartlett was a dirty, grimy place, frequently afflicted by clouds of sawdust from the saw-mill or coal dust from the coal-yard. When the wind was in the west heavy fumes from the lime kilns drifted across the area. The roads were muddy and full of pot-holes. Housing in the Cartlett area was generally of poor quality, and some of the terraces of working-class houses were not much better than slums. Crime was rife, and the local inns were patronised by many local characters who would not have been welcome in the "posh" inns of the town centre.

Once upon a time the manager of the Cartlett corn mill became convinced that one of his staff was systematically stealing quantities of flour. He could not be sure, and so one day he laid a trap by making a careful note of the number of sacks stored at the end of the day's work. Sure enough, next morning one of the sacks was missing. He had his suspicions as to who was responsible, but none of the staff would say anything and he had no evidence to go on. There was nothing for it but to consult Abe Biddle, the Wise Man of Millin Dingle, who lived not far outside the town. On hearing the story, the Wise Man said that he already knew the culprit. "leave it to me," he said. "Go back to the mill, and next time a sack is stolen the person responsible will be marked for all to see."

Sure enough, some days later the manager discovered that another sack of flour had disappeared. Immediately he summoned all his workers to line up against a wall, and noticed that one of the women had part of her face covered with a thick head-scarf. He challenged her to remove it, and she reluctantly obeyed, to reveal a strange "excrescence" of skin on her cheek. The miserable woman said that it had suddenly appeared, and some of her fellow workers remarked that it had the shape of a sack of flour. On being pressed by the manager, she confessed to the thefts from the mill. She was immediately dismissed, and the strange mark on her face did not disappear till she had paid for all of the flour which she had stolen.

Date: c 1840   *Source: Hall and Hall p 467*

5.5 The Healing Stone at Bridell

In some parts of Pembrokeshire there is still a strong belief in "folk medicine," and of course modern techniques of healing through the use of herbs and other materials have simply re-awakened memories of methods which are thousands of years old. Charms and strange efficacious medicines and pills were widely used before the advent of modern medicine, and there are many nineteenth-century records of "miraculous" cures which modern scientists find difficult to explain.

In the early 1800's there were a number of "quack doctors" who travelled through West Wales carrying with them healing stones. One such stone was referred to as "Llaethfaen". It was a small white pebble, slightly smaller than a hen's egg, and it was supposed to have miraculous properties. In particular, it was used as a preventative or cure for hydrophobia or rabies; if somebody had been bitten by a mad dog they would be given a milk mixture containing a small quantity of powder scraped off the stone, and this would guarantee that they would not be affected by rabies. Llaethfaen was kept at Gilfachwen, near Llandysul, and many hundreds of people were given the milk mixture over the years, especially during the summer months when rabid dogs had a tendency to go mad. In every case, the treatment was successful.

When Iolo Morgannwg was travelling in Pembrokeshire in 1802, he came across a crowd of people near Bridell Church. In their midst was a man extolling the virtues of a healing stone called Llysfaen. He was well into his sales pitch, claiming that it was "an infallible remedy for the canine madness". Apparently he had a good supply of the stone. He said that it was only to be found up in the mountains after a thunder-storm, and that only those with special powers could see it and collect it. He was selling a powder scraped off the stone for five shillings an ounce (a great deal of money in those days), and said that the powder had to be mixed with milk and then drunk by the afflicted person.

Much intrigued, Iolo asked to see the stone, and when the man handed it to him he said "Why, this is simply a piece of ordinary Glamorgan alabaster! There is nothing special about it at all!" At this, the man blushed and appeared confounded. Then he became very angry, and protested that the treatment was known to have worked well on many occasions. And much to Iolo's surprise the assembled country folk sprang to the healer's defence. One person after another shouted that they had seen the hydrophobia cured in dogs and in human beings who had drunk the powder and milk mixture. And it was explained to Iolo that the proper method was for the afflicted person to eat or drink nothing but the powdered milk for nine days, after which time a cure was guaranteed. In no uncertain terms, he was told to mind his own business. Duly impressed by this show of public support for the mysterious powers of Llysfaen, Iolo was not inclined to continue the discussion. He beat a hasty retreat from the angry customers, leaving the salesman fully in control of the situation.

Date: 1802   *Source: Davies p 288*

5.6 The Llanwnda Pills

Once upon a time a young lady who lived in Llanwnda was cleaning the windows of her cottage. It was a hot and humid day, with thunder in the air. The weather looked somewhat threatening, but as the black clouds piled up over Pencaer she carried on with her work, thinking that if a thunder-storm was to break she would get plenty of warning and would be able to retreat indoors in good time. However, with no warning whatsoever a mighty flash of lightning struck the nearby rocks of Garnwnda and there was a simultaneous crash of thunder, the like of which she had never heard before.

Quite literally, the poor girl was frightened out of her wits by this experience. She collapsed on the ground, and her family had to carry her indoors. She recovered somewhat, but from that day on she suffered from epileptic fits. Her family did not know what to do, and the family doctor could do little to help. At last a local *Dyn hysbys* or magician was consulted, and he gave clear instructions as to what should be done. The girl's father agreed to do as the magician suggested, but the poor girl was told nothing. A few weeks later a local person died, and the parish grave-digger started to dig a grave in the old Llanwnda churchyard. The father went along to keep an eye on things, and sure enough, as the magician had predicted, some old human bones were uncovered in the grave. They were thrown out onto the pile of soil.

The father collected one of these bones, took it home and cleaned it carefully. Then, following the instructions he had been given, he ground it down into a fine powder which he made into pills. These pills were given to the girl, who took them obediently. And from that day on she was completely cured of her epileptic fits.

Date: c 1880   *Source: Davies p 290*

Her family did not know what to do, and the family doctor could do little to help.

5.7 The Man who Knew too Much

In Twelfth Century Pembrokeshire there were a number of strange individuals whom we would refer to nowadays as soothsayers or sorcerers. Giraldus Cambrensis, writing around 1189 in his book **The Description of Wales**, describes them as *Awenyddion*, which means literally poets or those who speak in a trance or frenzy. It was commonly believed that such people were possessed by devils.

When a soothsayer was consulted about day-to-day problems he would go into a trance and lose control of his senses. He would not answer questions in any logical way. He would pour out a torrent of words which were incoherent and apparently meaningless to most of those who heard them; but the "client" could sometimes be given a solution to his problem if he paid very close attention. After the trance the soothsayer would recover as if waking from heavy sleep, and would have to be shaken violently before regaining full control of his senses. Once fully awake, he would remember nothing of what had transpired during the trance.

According to Giraldus the utterances of the soothsayers were a strange mixture of ignorance and inspiration, and he speculated that they were given the gift of divination through visions and dreams. Some of them invoked the True and Living God while in a trance but others were said to be possessed by demons or even by the devil. The common people believed that soothsayers possessed some secret knowledge not given to normal mortals. For this reason they inspired great fear when they were in their trances. They were said to be able to perform signs and miracles. They spoke with strange tongues, and many of them were given an uncanny knowledge of the future.

One of the strangest stories given in the writings of Giraldus concerns a man called Meilyr, who hailed originally from the city of Caerleon. He was a soothsayer who was reputed to be able to explain the occult and foretell the future. When he was a young man he was very much in love with a young lady who lived near the city. One Palm Sunday he met his beloved out in the country in a peaceful and beautiful spot, and it seemed to both of them too good an opportunity to be missed. Meilyr was enjoying himself in her arms and "tasting her delights" when suddenly instead of the beautiful girl he found in his embrace a horrible hairy creature with long rough hair and a face too terrible to look upon. The experience was so profound that his wits deserted him and he became, in an instant, quite mad. He remained in this condition for many years, and eventually he was sent to the Monastery of St David's in the hope that he might there recover his sanity.

The saintly monks of St David's nursed him back to health; and at last he was able to resume his place in the community. But for the rest of his life he retained a close familiarity with unclean spirits. He was able to see them, recognise them, and call them each by his own name. According to the people he would talk to them as if they were close friends, and they would assist him in solving problems and in foretelling the future. Some said that he knew far too much for his own good. He was particularly adept at foretelling events in the near neighbourhood, and many people sought his assistance if they had been victims of some crime.

In his dealings with familiar spirits, Meilyr would often describe them as appearing in the form of huntsmen with horns hanging around their necks. Apparently he did not have many dealings with animal spirits, unlike some of the other soothsayers. If someone should tell a lie in his presence, Meilyr would immediately be aware of it, for he would see a demon dancing on the liar's tongue. If he looked at a book which contained some false statement, or which aimed to deceive the reader, he could immediately put his finger on the offending passage. When asked how he could do this, he would say that a demon was pointing out the falsehood for him. When he visited the dormitory of the Monastery at St David's he would point to the bed of any monk who harboured false thoughts, and he would denounce those who were afflicted by the vices of lust, gluttony, and greed.

Giraldus described a number of incidents by which Meilyr had caused severe embarrassment to those around him. On one occasion he revealed in confidence to Cynan, the good and saintly Abbot of Whitland, that he had received a vision of a local woman, and asked the Abbot whether he had anything to do with her. On this the holy man wept, and confessed to Meilyr that he had lusted after her. The Abbot allowed himself to be whipped by three of his monks, this being his punishment.

On another occasion Meilyr predicted the downfall of Enoch the Abbot of Strata Marcella. He said that the Abbot would be ruined, for on that very day he would run off with a nun, thereby causing great scandal within the ecclesiastical community. Strata Marcella was a long way away, but people noted the date on which Meilyr had made his prophecy; and sure enough, eight days later news came through from distant parts that the Abbot had indeed run off with a nun, and was in disgrace. When Meilyr was asked how it was that he could be aware of such an event more than 100 miles away, he simply said that he had learned of it from a demon in the guise of a huntsman who had visited him early in the morning. Interestingly enough, in this case also the sinner came to repent. Enoch returned to his monastery a humble and chastened man, and according to the brothers in the Monastery he became stronger and more saintly following his experience.

Meilyr continued to embarrass the great and the good with his prophecies and insights for the rest of his life. In the year 1174, having left the sanctuary of St David's, he was in Usk Castle. He prophesied that some weeks later the castle would be attacked by the Earl of Clare, and that he himself would be wounded in military action. He said that the castle would fall to the enemy, but that he would escape from Usk alive. And so it came to pass. Meilyr was very badly injured in the battle. He escaped, but died soon afterwards from his wounds.

Commenting on Meilyr's sad end, Giraldus was clearly uncertain whether to treat the soothsayer as a friend or enemy of God. On balance he seems to have considered Meilyr to have been on the side of the devil, and his epitaph was as follows: "The Enemy knows how to favour his friends, but this is how he rewards them in the end".

Date: c 1160   *Source: Giraldus p 246 & p 116*

5.8 Moll and the Ill-fated Sheep

Moll of Redberth was a famous witch who lived in the early Nineteenth Century in a little cottage on the road from Carew to Begelly. Many stories were in circulation in the Carew area about her evil powers, and there is no doubt that most of the local people were frightened of her. After she died it was said that she had confessed on her deathbed to the parish priest that she had been a witch for 37 years. She confessed to having harmed scores of people with her spells, and told the priest how she had acquired her occult powers. Apparently, as a young woman attending her first communion service in Carew Cheriton church, she had not eaten the bread but had kept it in her hand. Then, on the way home from church, she had fed the sacred bread to a dog on the road. "I thus gave unto Satan the body of my Lord," she said. "And in return he gave to me the power to bewitch."

In the shearing season of 1841 Moll went to a farmer near Carew to ask if she could have a little fleece with which to spin some woollen yarn. The farmer refused, since Moll was always begging for things, and the old woman went on her way muttering threats. "Just you wait," she said. "You will soon wish you had been more civil with me, for something terrible is about to happen." The farmer watched her as she went up the farm lane. He saw that she stopped at a field gate, opened it and went into the field. Then she counted carefully the sheep that were in the field. There were 31 fine ewes, all newly shorn. She looked at them carefully, then left the field, closed the gate and went on her way.

By the evening all 31 sheep were dead. The farmer was distraught, since they were extremely valuable animals, but there was nothing he could do. How could he prove to anybody that Moll was responsible? But to his dying day he claimed that Old Moll had cast "the evil eye" onto his sheep, and that the blame lay entirely at her door.

Date: 1841   *Source: Meredith Morris p 21*

5.9 How Pryderi Lost the Pigs

Math son of Mathonwy was lord of Gwynedd. Unless there happened to be a war going on he enjoyed the comfortable life, and his constant companion was Goewin, the fairest virgin anybody had ever seen. It so happened that Math had two nephews named Gilfaethwy and Gwydion, who were fine warriors but not to be trusted. Indeed, Gwydion was a bard and a magician, although Math was unaware of his supernatural powers. Gilfaethwy was madly in love with the fair Goewin, and his love-sickness was so obvious that his brother at last asked him (although he knew the answer) what was causing his grey face and wasted body. So Gwydion promised that he would obtain Goewin for his brother; and he set in motion a terrible course of events.

The two brothers went to Math. "Lord," said Gwydion, "I have heard that in the South there are such creatures as have never been seen before -- small creatures they are, with flesh better than oxen." Math was intrigued. "What is their name?" he asked. "They are called *Hobeu or Moch* (hogs or swine), Lord," replied Gwydion. "And they belong to Pryderi son of Pwyll, prince of Dyfed. They were given to Pwyll as a present from Arawn King of the Otherworld. And they are kept at Cwm Cych in Dyfed." Math and Pryderi were old enemies, and Math rose to the bait and thought it would be a good idea to steal the pigs from Dyfed. "By what means can they be got from Pryderi?" asked the prince. Gwydion replied that it could be done, and offered to set out to Dyfed with eleven others disguised as bards. Math agreed, and so the plan was set in motion.

When Gwydion and his accomplices found Pryderi he was in his court in Cardigan. They were invited into the court, and as chief bard Gwydion sat beside Pryderi for the evening meal. After the feast Pryderi asked Gwydion to entertain the court with a tale, and since he was the best storyteller in the world he entertained them in the most splendid fashion. Afterwards he was warmly congratulated by all the members of the court, and Pryderi was delighted. "Now Lord, may I tell you my errand, for can anybody tell it better than myself?" "You have a right good tongue, sure enough," replied Pryderi. "Tell me your errand." Then Gwydion said that he had come to ask for the strange animals that had come from Annwn, the Otherworld. Pryderi replied that he could not give them away, for there was a covenant between him and his country that he would not give them away or sell any of them until they had multiplied to double their number. "Lord, do not worry," said the silken-tounged Gwydion. "I can free you from your covenant. Do not give me the swine tonight, but do not refuse me. Tomorrow I will show you a most marvellous exchange."

So they all went to bed. When Gwydion and his accomplices were in their lodgings they discussed the matter, and the accomplices were down-hearted when they heard of Pryderi's determination to keep the swine. But Gwydion was not to be put off, and as the men watched he began to practice his magic arts. He made by magic twelve stallions and twelve greyhounds, each of them pitch black but white-breasted, with gold harnesses and collars and leashes, and solid gold saddles on the backs of the prancing horses. Nobody had ever seen such magnificent animals before. Then he made twelve golden shields out of toadstools.

Next morning Gwydion took the stallions and the greyhounds and the shields to the court, and all the nobles were astonished. He met Pryderi and said "Good day to you, Lord. I have brought to you the finest horses and the finest hounds in the world, with saddles and harnesses and leashes of such gold as the world has never seen. I have brought gold shields for the riders of the stallions. I know that you may not give or sell the swine because of your covenant; but exchange them you may." Pryderi remembered the warning of his father Pwyll that he must never betray the trust of Arawn or abuse the gift; but he was sorely tempted by the treasures offered by Gwydion, and after taking counsel with his nobles he agreed to the exchange.

So the swine were fetched from Cwm Cych and handed over to Gwydion in exchange for the stallions, greyhounds and golden artifacts. Then the conspirators took their leave and rode off towards Gwynedd, driving the swine before them. As they travelled Gwydion urged his men to travel faster, and revealed that the spell would wear off after one day. They travelled across Ceredigion and Powys for five days; and on the sixth day they made a sty for the swine near Llechwedd.

When the creations of the magician disappeared into thin air after one day Pryderi was furious, and realised that he had been tricked by the men of Gwynedd. He sent messages to all the cantrefs of Dyfed, summoning thousands of his men to battle. When Math heard that the men of Dyfed were being called to arms he was mystified, but then he realised that Gwydion had caused the trouble, and determined to try and make peace. Gwydion and his men at last arrived at the court of Gwynedd. He deflected the wrath of his master by talking about the swine, and said that they were in a pigsty at Llechwedd. Math could not resist going to see the strange animals, and set off with a small band of retainers. When he was away Gwydion and his brother Gilfaethwy forced their way into the royal household, and there, on Math's own bed, Gilfaethwy raped the beautiful Goewin.

There followed such slaughter as Wales has never seen again, between the armies of Dyfed and the armies of Gwynedd. Math did not learn of the rape of Goewin until later, since he was preoccupied with the war. Thousands of warriors fell as one battle followed another. At last, wearied by the terrible sufferings of his men, Pryderi sent a message to Math offering to settle the matter in personal combat with Gwydion, the evil magician who had caused all the trouble. Reluctantly Math agreed, and a place was selected at Maentwrog for the combat between Pryderi and Gwydion. A fearsome struggle ensued, but Gwydion used magic and enchantment to slay the brave Prince of Dyfed. So Pryderi died, and the war came to an end.

It appeared that evil had triumphed. However, Math too was a magician, and when he heard from Goewin that she had been violated by the brothers Gwydion and Gilfaethwy he determined that justice should be done. He led them into a trap and struck them with his magic wand, turning them into a stag and a hind for a year, and a wild boar and a wild sow for a further year, and a wolf and a she-wolf for a third year. So, having cruelly betrayed all the higher feelings of men, they became wild animals hunted by men in the dark, damp forests of Gwynedd.......

Date: 800 - 900 AD?   *Source: Jones & Jones p 57*

5.10 Tom Eynon the Witch

Tom Eynon was feared by almost everybody. He lived at The Rock, near Lamphey, and it was well known that if you happened to get on the wrong side of him he was quite likely to "cast the evil eye" on you, leading to endless trouble. There were various tales in circulation around 1840, one of which involved a bewitching of a butter churn. But then things rebounded on Tom, much to the delight of the locals.

Tom was married twice. He treated his first wife very harshly, and never gave her sufficient money to pay for food and other household needs. The poor woman led a miserable existence, and matters were not helped by the way in which most of the locals kept well clear of her husband. When she died, Tom waited for a respectable period of time and then he married again. The locals felt sorry for the new wife, assuming that the poor woman would have just as miserable a time as her predecessor. Right in the middle of the wedding night, at a very embarrassing moment, who should appear next to the bed but the very angry ghost of Tom's first wife. "Tom! Tom!" she cried. "Give me some money, give me some money!" Tom's new wife was terrified by the apparition and fled downstairs. Tom was very angry but perhaps not very surprised, since he had frequent encounters with the spirit world. He knew how to get rid of ghosts, and drove the phantom away. However, nothing would induce his new wife to return to bed that night, and indeed she was so frightened by the experience that it took many weeks before he could coax her back to the marriage bed. This episode did no good at all for Tom's sex life, and it caused much amusement in the local community. Needless to say, after this, he treated his second wife considerably better than his first.

Date: c 1840   *Source: Meredith Morris p 101*

He treated his first wife very harshly, and never gave her sufficient money to pay for food and other household needs.

5.11 The Bewitched Cartwheel

Thomas Evans lived at Molleston Mountain, not far from Narberth. One evening he was returning home in his old-fashioned dog-cart from Haverfordwest Market. On the way he passed Deep Lake at the foot of Arnold's Hill. There he passed Old Ben Volke, who was also returning from Market, but on foot. Old Ben lived in a hovel near Canaston Bridge, and he was reputed to be a witch. "How be yer Tom?" said Ben. "Oh, middlin. How be yerself, Ben?" said Tom, as he passed by, giving his pony a whip. Old Ben was heavily laden, and had hoped for a lift. He was clearly not amused, and scowled under his battered hat, but Tom was in a hurry and thought no more of it.

Soon Tom was far ahead and was starting up the hill. Looking behind him, he saw Old Ben in the distance, standing beneath a tall yew tree. A shiver ran up his spine as he thought that he could see other dark shapes moving in the dark November shadows. As he watched he saw Ben light his pipe, but instead of seeing the expected spark he saw flashes of lightning striking out in all directions. He felt the hair rising on the back of his neck, and cracked his whip in order to urge his pony onwards. Suddenly the cart skidded to a halt, with the right wheel totally jammed. Tom dismounted, but could find nothing which was obviously wrong. As soon as he stood beside the cart the wheel revolved quite freely. He thought he had better walk alongside the horse and cart until he reached the top of the long hill. Then, feeling quite exhausted, he climbed back onto the cart and urged the pony on. Again the wheel jammed and the cart would not move.

After this, Tom repeatedly climbed onto the cart and alighted, with the same result each time. Whenever he was seated snugly on board, the wheel would not move; whenever he walked alongside, the wheel moved quite freely. Now convinced that Ben had bewitched the wheel, Tom thought that there was nothing for it but to walk home alongside his cart, for a distance of six miles or more. He was not amused.

On the following Monday, Tom went to see Abe Biddle the magician, who lived in Millin Dingle. The great man consulted his book of mysteries, and confirmed that Ben Volke had bewitched the cartwheel. Then he told Tom how to break the spell. He had to take an iron nail and dip it into the blood of a toad. Then he had to drive it into a particular part of the wheel with a new iron hammer. The hammer had to have a handle of "rontree" wood (rowan or mountain ash). Tom followed the instructions exactly, and the spell was broken. After that the wheel gave him no trouble whatsoever.

Date: c 1803?   *Source: Meredith Morris p 29*

5.12 Moll and the Bucket of Culm

It was a dark and drizelly day in November 1842, with a cold wind blowing in from the west. Billy Morris of Dairy Hays, on the edge of the hamlet of Carew Cheriton, was not looking forward to a long journey which he knew would leave him wet and miserable, but his culm supply was almost finished, and he had to go to Bonville's Court Colliery for another cart-load if he was to keep the home fire burning. So he prepared his heavy cart, harnessed his two best cart-horses, put on his waterproofs and set off along the road to Saundersfoot.

Billy bought his culm from the pit-head at a reasonable price and set off for home with the drizzle still swirling about him. The load was heavy and the five-mile journey slow. At last he reached Redberth, and with less than two miles to go he allowed himself the luxury of thinking about his warm fireside. As he passed through the village he saw Old Moll standing at the door of her clom cottage. She begged him to give her a bucketful of culm for her fire; but he was in a hurry to get home and he ignored her as he drove past. He knew that Old Moll was a witch, but he was in no mood to mollify her since she was always asking for things and never gave anything in return.

He had not gone fifty yards up the road when the cart tipped over backwards, flinging him off his driving seat and depositing the whole load of culm in the middle of the road. At the same time the cart-horse harnesses came loose, freeing the two horses, upon which they galloped off into the distance. Billy was furious, and chased off after them, shaking his fist in the air and shouting at the top of his voice. At this Moll quietly came out of her cottage with a bucket and a little shovel. She filled the bucket with culm and went back inside.

When Billy at last returned, having collected his two cart-horses, he discovered that the back end of the cart was broken. Feeling fed up to the back teeth, he harnessed up the horses again and started to load the culm back onto the damaged cart with his big shovel. While he was in the middle of his heavy labour Old Moll came out of her cottage again and looked on with a grin on her face. "I suppose ye don't mind that I helped meself to a bucket of culm just now, Billy," she said. "I sees that thy cart is summat smaller than t'was, an' won't hold so much culm, so I thought I'd save yer from havin' two journeys to fetch it home."

Date: 1842   *Source: Meredith Morris p 21*

5.13 Moll and the Bewitched Cream

Sarah Cole lived at a cottage called The Bog, not far from Upper Nash. She kept three cows and churned her milk every week, taking 6 lbs of butter quite regularly to Pembroke Market, where she exchanged it for groceries. One fine morning, as she was putting some fresh cream into the churn, Old Moll called at the door, begging. Sarah had no time for the old woman, for she had work to do, and she turned her away. Moll said not a word, but she was mortally offended, and immediately "cast the evil eye" on the cream. When she had gone Sarah started the churning, but on this occasion the tedious work went on and on all day without the cream even beginning to separate. At dusk Sarah was feeling exhausted and had to give up the task, having made no progress at all in setting the butter. She became quite convinced that Old Moll had cast a spell on her cream.

Sarah went outside into the back-yard in order to get some fresh air, and there, in the fading daylight, she was surprised to see on her gatepost a black glutinous mass which was known to country people as "witches' butter". (Nowadays we know it to be a fungus, with the Latin name *Exida tremella*.) On seeing this Sarah knew what to do, for she had heard about witches' butter from her parents. She knew that the strange black substance was a part of the spell that Old Moll had cast on her cream. She went back into the house, heated up her poker in the fire until it was white hot, and then she attacked the enemy. As she thrust the poker into the witches' butter it spat and hissed and then dissolved into a cloud of foul-smelling steam. This broke the spell. Sarah heard a strange groaning noise as the evil power was broken; and then she heard a loud noise like a flock of birds flapping their wings.

Confident that the evil power had now departed, Sarah returned to her churning, and in no time at all she had a quantity of excellent butter to take to Pembroke Market next day.

Date: c 1840   *Source: Meredith Morris p 22*

5.14 Abe Biddle and the Church Window

Saturday night was a time of heavy drinking in the village of Hubberston.
One Sunday morning the congregation of Hubberston Church turned up
for Matins to discover that the beautiful east window of the church had
been smashed in. The parishioners were distraught, and although suspicion
fell on several local persons who were renowned for their love of the
bottle, no evidence was to be found as to the guilty party. The church
wardens met together to discuss the matter, and someone suggested that a
deputation should be sent to Abe Biddle, who lived at Millin Dingle, not
far from Haverfordwest. The vicar agreed, and so off they went to see the
great man.

Abe invited the men into his little cottage, and they were interested to
see that he lived in a sort of cosy simplicity. He was a big man with long
hair, and when he moved about he used a stout walking stick. But he was
tidily dressed, and he had an efficient and courteous manner. He invited
them to sit down and asked them to tell their story. Abe listened intently,
and then he went to the corner of the room and fetched his magic mirror.
He placed it before them, and as they watched in silence a face appeared in
the glass, first very faintly and then with some clarity. Immediately the
men recognised the face as that of a local man who had long held a grudge
against the vicar. "Maybe we cannot get recompense for the broken
window," they said. "But can you help in bringing the wickedness of this
deed home to the villain?"

"Just leave the matter in my hands," said Abe. "I'll both bring the deed
home to his heart, and also mete out to him a proper punishment." And so
the men from Hubberston took their leave and went on their way.

On the following Sunday morning, as the good people of the village
were present at Matins, the service was interrupted by a great commotion
outside. Through the windows the parishioners could see a man rushing
aimlessly and wildly back and forth on the bank close to the church. The
bank was covered in thick gorse bushes, but the man rushed back and
forth through the bushes, apparently unable to stop himself. Every now
and then he squealed like a stuck pig or shrieked like a demon as he
tripped and fell headlong into one or other of the gorse bushes. The
astonishment of the congregation at last turned to consternation, as the
good people feared that the man would seriously hurt himself. But at last
he ran madly into the church. He rushed up the aisle, and then fell onto
his knees in front of the altar, gasping for breath and covered with cuts
and scratches. There, in a loud voice, he confessed that it was he who had
smashed the church window while in a drunken stupor, and he begged
the vicar and the congregation for pardon.

Needless to say, the priest and congregation showed their Christian
charity and forgave the poor man, who had clearly suffered enough for his
crime. Thenceforth he became a regular church member and a good
Christian gentleman. Presumably he also gave up the bottle.

Date: c 1820   *Source: Meredith Morris p 26*

5.15 John Adolph's Mercy Mission

John Adolph lived at Garron Pill, one of the creeks on the eastern shore of the Daugleddau River. His little daughter was seriously ill, and John feared for her life. He became quite convinced that she had been bewitched by the famous black witches who lived at Garron. No-one could help her, and at last John was advised by a friend to go and see Abe Biddle in his cottage at Millin Dingle.

On his way to see the wise man, John hurt his foot, and he was limping quite badly by the time he reached Abe's cottage. He knocked on the door and was invited inside, and the great man listened in silence to the story of the little girl's illness. Then Abe mixed up a bottle of medicine for the child, and gave it to the worried father. He then urged John to hurry home as fast as he could go, for he said that the girl was very close to death. At this, John became desperately concerned. "To hurry, Sir, is my reasonable duty," he said. "But to reach home soon is quite out of the question, the road being so rough and my foot being injured." "I suppose you are right," said Abe. "But don't you worry, for I'll give you a lift. Good night!" And with that he disappeared back into the cottage and closed the door.

John Adolph set off on his way, hurrying up the hill above the dingle and limping badly. In a cold sweat and fearing for the life of his daughter he looked at his watch and saw that it was a quarter to ten. After a couple of minutes he reached the top of the hill and came to a crossroads. As he approached he saw a magnificent white horse, saddled and bridled, trotting towards him. Remembering Abe's parting words and believing that he was meant to use the horse, John pulled himself into the saddle and grasped the reins. Then the creature arched its neck and with a shrill neigh it was away. John had never ridden such a majestic beast. He felt that he was flying, and he had no sensation of the horse touching the ground. It galloped so swiftly that John could hardly breathe. Below him he saw the muddy estuary of the Eastern Cleddau at Landshipping. At last, after only a few minutes John saw his house below him, and the horse descended at Garron Gate, only about one hundred yards from the Pill. John dismounted, and he watched as the horse cantered off up the road. It disappeared in a sheet of white flame.

John rushed into the house and quickly gave the medicine to his little daughter who was now hardly breathing and was obviously close to death. Immediately the little girl began to breathe more easily, and John was able to relax. Then he looked at his watch, and he discovered that it was eight minutes to ten. Only seven minutes had passed since he had last looked at his watch, and he had travelled a distance of six miles over land and water on the back of the white horse. The journey itself could not have lasted for more than four minutes.

After this the little girl quickly recovered, and John remained grateful to Abe Biddle for the rest of his life. He never forgot the white horse, but he never saw it again.

Date: c 1830   *Source: Meredith Morris p 28*

5.16 The Killing at Clyn

David Llewellyn lived at a farm called Clyn, near Cilrhedyn in the Gwaun Valley. He was involved in a bitter feud with a neighbour. He had a fine pony in a field near the farmhouse, and one day when he went to feed it he found that it had been shot. The poor animal lay dead in the middle of the field. There were no clues as to the culprit, but Mr Llewellyn had little doubt that his unpleasant neighbour had been the man responsible. When accused of the dastardly deed the man denied all knowledge of what had happened.

At length Mr Llewellyn decided that he would go to consult the famous *Dyn hysbys* Dr Joseph Harris of Werndew, near Dinas. When he arrived in the doctor's consulting room he explained that his best pony had been shot, and that he was seeking help in discovering the culprit. Dr Harris listened intently, and then said "Do you see that large mirror on my wall? Look into it very carefully. However, do not frown or laugh or make any movement of your head while you are staring into the glass." Obediently David Llewellyn looked into the mirror. "Now," said Dr Harris, "I will show you the person in the very act of shooting your pony. But are you sure that you can look at this event without any movement of your head? If you move, you will forever be afflicted with whatever movement you make." "Yes, yes," said David Llewellyn. "I promise I will not move at all." "Very well," said the doctor. "I will now leave the room and let you look very carefully into the glass."

As Mr Llewellyn looked intently into the mirror, the glass cleared, and he saw his neighbour, together with another man whom he had previously assumed to be a friend, approach his pony with a gun. The neighbour took aim at the pony's head and fired. A loud gunshot rang out, and the pony dropped dead onto the ground. So surprised was Mr Llewellyn by the noise that he blinked and gasped. After that, although he knew who had shot his pony, poor Mr Llewellyn was always afflicted with a blink and a stammer.

Date: c 1840   *Source: Meredith Morris p 82*

5.17 The Goblin at Southernpits

There are not many stories in Pembrokeshire about goblins, and there is some doubt among the experts as to whether they belong to the realm of ghosts, fairies or demons. In the Welsh tradition the word *Bwca* or *Pwca* is used for a goblin or elf, but the *Bwca* is normally attached to a particular house or cottage and performs some sort of service to the residents. He is comparatively harmless, but is more like a familiar spirit than a fairy, and in many stories he is associated with the signs and symbols of magic or witchcraft. This story comes from the Lawrenny district.

Once upon a time there was an old cottage at Sudden Pits, not far from Coedcenlas on the road to Cresselly. Nowadays it is called Southernpits. An old couple lived in the cottage in abject poverty. One winter's night, very late, the old man had gone to bed and his wife was tidying up in the kitchen and preparing to follow him. She heard a very strange noise outside in the yard, and for a moment she listened at the door, becoming convinced that something or someone was coming towards the house. She decided that it was probably a heifer which had broken out of the neighbouring field, and so she went outside to drive it away. She was greatly surprised to see a strange looking goblin in the back yard. He was only a few yards away from the door and he was preoccupied in drawing a circle in the mud with a heavy club. The wife got such a shock that she screamed and started to close the door, but the goblin fixed her with a penetrating gaze so that she was unable to move. He spoke not a word but indicated to her through signals that she should fetch her husband. This she did and after getting dressed the old man came downstairs.

The old couple stood at the back door and watched the goblin complete the drawing of the circle in the mud. Then he stopped work and beckoned to the couple to follow him. He stopped in the corner of the yard and indicated to the old man that he should fetch a mattock and start to dig. Although he was very frightened by this strange experience the old man obeyed and dug a deep hole at the spot indicated. At last he came upon a large pottery jar and broke it with a single blow of the mattock. He was amazed and delighted when he saw that it contained hundreds of gold coins. The goblin smiled a strange goblin smile, showing his milk-white teeth, and a flame came out of his mouth. However, so preoccupied were the old couple with their wonderful discovery that they quite forgot to thank the goblin, and his pleasure turned to anger. He growled a frightful growl, and proceeded to beat the old couple with his club until they were black and blue. Then he lifted the club high above his head, and thunder and lightning came out of his mouth. Then, as they cowered in the corner of the yard, the old couple saw that on top of the hillock above the cottage there was a solid gold chariot drawn by two jet black boars and driven by two sleek greyhounds. The chariot came down the slope at breakneck speed, driven by the greyhounds as they cracked their whips. To the ears of the old couple the sound of the wheels was like the most terrible thunderstorm. The chariot came straight towards them, and they thought they would be run over; but it swerved, and as it passed they saw one of the greyhounds grab the goblin by the hair and drag him into the chariot. Then off they went into the distance like a hurricane, never to be seen again.

The old couple were almost scared out of their wits by this experience, but when all was quiet again they saw that the broken urn and the gold coins were still there in the hole. They gathered up the coins, filled in the hole, and thereafter continued for many years to enjoy their good fortune. Their rise from abject poverty to comfortable living was frequently commented upon by their neighbours, but they never revealed how they had come by their unexpected wealth.

Date: c 1810   *Source: Meredith Morris p 36*

5.18 William John's Aerial Journey

When the Rev Meredith Morris lived in the Gwaun Valley as a child, his uncle William John lived at Trewern, about a mile from Pontfaen. In 1872 William's wife fell seriously ill with inflammation of the lungs, and it transpired that the local doctor could do little to help. William became desperately worried as her health deteriorated, and at last it was suggested that he should go to see the famous magician Dr Joseph Harries of Werndew, near Dinas. It was too dark to take his horse, so William had to walk all the way, down into the Gwaun Valley, up the other side and over the wild moor of Mynydd Melyn.

At last he arrived, very late at night. He hammered on the door of the doctor's cottage, and the famous man let him in. He listened intently to William's account of his wife's symptoms, and immediately poured some special potion into a small bottle. He gave it to William. "Now," he said. "Get back to your wife as fast as you possibly can, for she is close to death even as I speak." William's heart sank. "I will, sir," he replied, "But the road is in a bad state, and the old footpath over Mynydd Melyn is even worse. There is no moon, and I can hardly see where I am going." The doctor nodded. "All right, I understand," he said. "Make your way as best you can to the top of the lane past Bryn, and then you will have a lift."

William John puffed and panted up the muddy lane, and when he reached the top he was utterly surprised and bewildered to be lifted upward and carried along through the air by some mysterious force. When he reached Trewern he looked at his pocket watch and discovered that his aerial journey in the pitch darkness over a distance of 5 miles had taken only 20 minutes. He was just in time to give the medicine to his wife, who had only a spark of life left in her. The medicine worked like magic, and very soon she was restored to full health.

Date: c 1872   *Source: Meredith Morris p 83*

PEMBROKESHIRE
FOLK TALES

SIGNS, OMENS AND PORTENTS

6.1 The Corpse Bird at Eglwyswrw

In many parts of Wales there was a belief in times past in the *Aderyn y gorff* or corpse bird, which would flap its wings against the window of a room as a portent of death. Sometimes it was believed that the death would occur in the room which had the affected window; but some people believed that the corpse bird could beat against any window in the doomed house. Maybe there is a deep psychological fear at work here, for even today most people dread the sight or the sound of a bird beating its wings against a window pane. This fear was no doubt reinforced by Alfred Hitchcock's famous film about birds.......

Contrary to what one might expect, the *Aderyn y gorff* is not a large black bird such as a crow or raven, but a small bird that would normally be thought of as harmless. Around 1870 Wirt Sikes found that the little bird would chirp at the door of the person who was about to die. But according to an old woman called Miss Griffiths who lived at Henllan, near Eglwyswrw, the corpse bird was very small and grey in colour. In the middle part of the last century she had four visits from this little bird. On each occasion it flapped at her bedroom window, first to warn of the death of her father, and then as an omen of the deaths of each of her three uncles in turn. We do not know whether the old lady had a fifth visit from the bird before her own death early in the present century......

Date: c 1860   *Source: Davies p 206*

.....the "Aderyn y gorff" is not a large black bird such as a crow or raven, but a small bird that would normally be thought of as harmless.

6.2 A Knight of the Open Road

Homeless people, vagabonds and tramps have been a part of the Pembrokeshire scene for hundreds of years. They have travelled the roads with few possessions, slept beneath the stars, worked here and there, and survived on charity. Many have appeared like shadows, passed through the leafy lanes of the county, and disappeared again, unrecognized and nameless. Others have "adopted" the area, liking its people, travelling on an annual circuit of towns and villages and regularly visiting households which could provide a bite to eat, or a cup of tea, or a few days' work.

Every tramp has his own story. The reasons for a life on the road may be poverty, mental illness, family troubles, or simply a sense of wanderlust. Some tramps were, and are, fugitives from justice. Others are unable or unwilling to cope with the complexities of modern life and opt - like those who join monastic orders - to "live lightly" with few possessions and few responsibilities. Many of them, over the years, have succumbed to the effects of cold and damp, and denied the benefits of medical help have died sad and lonely deaths in hedgerows, caves or farm outbuildings.

In the early years of this century Long Jim Herrington was known all over Pembrokeshire, from Angle to Mynachlogddu and from St David's to Saundersfoot. He came originally from Ireland, and his tall ragged figure was familiar on many farms, where he would appear once or twice a year begging for food and shelter. He used to smoke cheap tobacco in an old pipe, and carried all his possessions in a bag on his back.

One of the farms on Long Jim's circuit was Pennardd Llandissilio, near Clunderwen. He used to beg for food and old clothes there, and was always kindly received. Further, he could always be sure of a bed for the night in the hayrick -- on condition that he left his matches and tobacco in the farmhouse. On one occasion, around 1920, the farmer's wife, who was a good Christian lady, struck up a conversation with Jim about Jesus. She mentioned the need for prayer, and the need to save one's soul. Jim was not one for religion, and refused to be drawn. With a scowl on his face, he went on his lonely way. The wife shrugged her shoulders and assumed that she would see Jim again in twelve months' time.

Much to the woman's surprise, Jim reappeared a fortnight later. He looked not at all well, with a grey face, sunken cheeks and hunched shoulders. He must have had some sort of premonition. He was invited in to sit by the kitchen fire and given a hot mug of tea. Then he said "since I was here the other day, missus, I been thinkin' about what you was sayin' about Jesus an' such-like. Will you tell me more?" And so the farmer's wife told him the story of Jesus, and how he died to save the souls of all men. He sat there for a long time, listening intently. Then he got up and said "thank you, missus, for bein' so kind. Now I'll be on me way." And without a further word he opened the door and set off along the muddy lane.

A fortnight later Long Jim Hetherington was found dead in a field near Fishguard.

Date: 1920   *Source: Mrs Gwennie Davies*

6.3 The Halloween Death List

At the beginning of the Nineteenth Century there was a strange Halloween custom in the south-east corner of Pembrokeshire and in adjacent Carmarthenshire. An old farmer from Eglwyscummin parish, who died in 1875, was told about this custom by his father.

He said that when he was a young man, around 1800, somebody was appointed to every parish church in the area to go into the church on All Hallows Eve to hear the roll-call of all those in the parish who would die during the coming year. An old woman of Laugharne, who died in 1820, used to stand at the appointed time by the chancel window of the church, where she would distinctly hear the names pronounced. She said that she had first gone there many years before as a joke, but having heard the names called it was now her duty to attend on every successive Halloween until she herself was called to Heaven. The burden of her deadly knowledge was difficult to cope with, for had she divulged her secrets this would have caused great distress in the community. However, in the occasional unguarded moment she let something slip which greatly impressed those around her.

On one occasion a well-known lady of the town fell ill, and a little group of neighbours happened to be discussing her ailment. "she is very bad indeed," said one. "The doctor has been, and has said there is nothing to be done. He says she will die." On hearing this, the old woman who knew the death list said "No, she will not die. Her name was not called." And sure enough, the lady made a miraculous recovery, and survived for many years afterwards. On another occasion she predicted to a close friend that the funeral of a local man would take place very shortly in the parish church. The friend was surprised, for the gentleman concerned was apparently in the best of health. But some days later he fell ill and died, and the funeral took place as foretold.

Date: 1800   *Source: Curtis p 207*

6.4 The Cwm Gwaun Nightmare

Some years ago a Welsh historian was researching the family history of the Gwaun Valley, and during her studies she came across some references to a terrible event which had occurred near Pontfaen during the wars between the Normans and the Welsh princes. During a skirmish, a troop of enemy soldiers descended on the community and killed all the menfolk. Then, totally out of control, they ravished the women one by one and then drowned them in a pool of the river Gwaun.

One day, the historian was relating this tragic story to a local farmer who lived near Pontfaen. As she talked, a look of amazement came over his face. "This is indeed very strange," he said. "Only a fortnight ago a young lady knocked on my door and asked if she could walk down to the river across my field. She was from Llandysul, and as far as I know she had never been to this area before. She explained to me that she had been having nightmares, night after night, and that her dream was always the same. Apparently, in the dream, she was tortured and raped by a group of men, with her agony ending only as she slid into the water. Then, as the water closed over her, she found peace. And always, on waking, she knew that she had to travel to a certain place in the Gwaun Valley which she could see in her mind's eye. Not knowing the Gwaun valley, she resisted for a long time, but at last, as the dream was repeated over and again, she could resist no longer. So she drove over one day, travelling slowly along the valley road until she recognized the place. That was when she knocked on my door and asked to walk down to the river."

Apparently, having found the spot where the terrible deed had been done many centuries before, the girl exorcised the dream and travelled back to Llandysul. After that, all was well, and the farmer did not see her again.

Date: c 1985   *Source: word of mouth*

6.5 Hettie Howells the Visionist

Hettie Howells was a remarkable old woman who lived at Pontfaen in the Gwaun Valley. She was known personally to the Rev Meredith Morris who spent his childhood in the area around 1875. She had a reputation for visions and premonitions, and invariably she knew about deaths and funerals a fortnight before they happened. Her cottage was very close to the graveyard of Jabez Chapel, and she claimed that if she peeped out of her bedroom window at midnight she would always see a **Canwyll gorff** as a small quivering red light in the graveyard if a death was about to occur. She said that she could also see the light travelling about three yards above the road surface along the route that would be followed by the funeral procession. According to her, the light, having entered the grave-yard, would stop for a minute or two above a certain place, and this is where the burial would eventually take place. Then, she said, the light would be snuffed out. She was in the habit of informing a few of her closest neighbours when she saw a corpse candle, and invariably she would be right about her predictions. Some of the locals considered her visions as miracles, but others claimed that she was a witch.

One day a sceptical man from outside the valley was visiting Pontfaen, and he heard about Hettie's special powers. He did not believe a word of what he was told, and issued a challenge to the old woman. He asked her to let him know when next she saw a corpse candle in Jabez graveyard, and to let him know the precise position at which the light stopped before it disappeared. Hettie was somewhat aggrieved at this lack of trust, but she agreed to the man's request. After only a few days she sent a message to the sceptic. Apparently she had seen a light coming down the steep lane from Penrhiw and then past the Dyffryn Arms towards Jabez. However, she appeared somewhat puzzled and uncertain, as if doubting her own premonition, because the little light had stood over a spot in the graveyard where no burials had ever taken place before. This news was greeted with some hilarity by those who refused to believe in her special powers, for they also knew that all the burials took place at the other end of the graveyard.

Exactly a fortnight later a little child living at Penrhiw was taken ill with the croup and died. The funeral party came down the steep hill to Pontfaen and along the lane to Jabez. When the party reached the graveyard they were asked by the minister to move to the far end of the hallowed ground; he had apparently decided that the normal place for burials now had inadequate space for further graves, and he thought it wise to begin to use another area. The grave that had been opened up by the grave-digger was at the exact spot where Hettie had seen the corpse candle glowing before it disappeared. After that, nobody every disbelieved Hettie Howells again, and she continued to have her strange visions until the day that she died.

Date: c 1860   *Source: Meredith Morris p 85*

6.6 The Bedside Table

George Griffiths of Cresswell Quay lived with his old mother in a house which also doubled up as his cobbler's shop. He used a room downstairs to practise his trade, and he used the same room as his bedroom. At one end of the room was his workbench, and at the other his bed with a small round bedside table beside it. In the year 1853 he was working late, finishing off a pair of boots at his work-bench. Suddenly he noticed that his bedside table was moving about, as if being dragged or pushed by a hidden hand. He jumped up, amazed and not a little frightened, for he could see no explanation for the table's movement. As he watched, the table was dragged across the room, its legs scraping along the floor, and then it came to a stop near the window. George moved the table back to the bedside, but he was greatly bewildered by what had happened, and could not get it out of his mind.

A few weeks later his mother's old aunt named Phebe Phillips came to live in the house. After only a few days she fell ill and died. Her body was carried downstairs into the cobbler's shop, and the bedside table, which was normally located between the bed and the wall, was dragged out and put near the window. Then some planks were placed on it and the body was properly laid out. Suddenly George's hair stood on end as he realized that the movement of the table, and the sounds it had made on the floor, were exactly those which had frightened him a few weeks earlier. Without realising it at the time, he had heard the *Tolaeth*.

Date: 1853   *Source: Meredith Morris p 87*

6.7 Strange Light at Cresswell Quay

It was a cold winter's night in 1850, and young George Griffiths was out for a walk beneath the sparkling frosty heavens. He lived at Cresswell Quay, which at that time was a bustling trading centre, with small vessels coming and going on the tide and carrying cargoes of coal, limestone and agricultural products. The lime kiln not far from the quay was burning brightly, and George decided that he would go and sit on top of the kiln for a little while in order to keep warm. As he sat there he looked down towards the blacksmith's shop, and was surprised to see a light moving towards him. At first he assumed that he was looking at a man carrying a lantern, but as it approached he realized that he could see no trace of either a man or a lantern. It became apparent that he was looking at a pale red ball of light which was moving along about eight or nine feet above the road surface. George became very frightened and he felt his hair standing on end. As he watched the light went slowly up the hill towards Pisgah Chapel. Then it disappeared. Afterwards George told several people about his strange experience. About a fortnight later old Betty Prickett died. Her funeral procession went along precisely the same route as the little light which George had seen; it went up the hill towards Pisgah, where the body was buried in the chapel graveyard.

Date: 1850   *Source: Meredith Morris p 88*

6.8 Betsy Morgan and the Cemetery

Betsy Morgan of Cresselly died in the year 1892, but for the ten years or so before her death she frequently saw corpse candles moving towards a field not far from her house. The candles would stop in the field, hover for a moment and then disappear. Her family and friends who knew about such things were surprised, since corpse candles were usually taken as signs of funeral processions to come, and they were supposed to disappear in graveyards at the position selected for the burial.

About a year after Betsy died Mr H Seymour Allen of Cresselly donated a parcel of land to the Primitive Methodists of the village, and on this land they built a new chapel with a commodious surrounding graveyard. By the time the Reverend Meredith Morris had come to the village in 1895 there had already been several burials in the new graveyard. The routes followed by the funeral processions were exactly those seen by Betsy in her visions, and the graves which were opened for the burials were in exactly the places where Betsy had seen the corpse candles disappear. In her lifetime she could not possibly have known that a future graveyard would be located in the field, for it was not even spoken about as a possibility before Mr Seymour Allen made his sudden and generous gift.

Date: c 1890   *Source: Meredith Morris p 88*

6.9 Premonition at Pisgah

Early one morning, while it was still dark, Mr John Thomas of Pisgah, Cresselly, heard a very strange omen. He was woken by a cry which seemed to be very close, and the voice was immediately recognizeable as that of his sister. The voice came, so far as he could make out, from near the front door of his cottage. "Mother! Mother!" said the voice, over and over again. John got up out of bed and opened the door but there was no sign of anyone. So he went to the back door and opened that, and could still see no sign of anyone. His old mother who was in the house was woken up with all the commotion; and both of them were very mystified because John's sister was away on holiday at the time. A few weeks later the sister was back at home, and John had almost forgotten about the strange incident. But then she was taken seriously ill, and within a few hours she had become delirious. In her delirium she shouted out "Mother! Mother!" over and over again, in exactly the voice which John had heard some weeks before. John was quite convinced that the phantom voice was a warning or "foretoken" of a forthcoming dangerous illness. Happily his sister did not die, but made a full recovery.

Date: 1881   *Source: Meredith Morris p 89*

6.10 Phantom Funeral at Llanddewi Velfrey

Billy Thomas was a postman who seems to have had some special ability for seeing the inhabitants of the spirit world. In later life he lived in Pembroke, but in 1874 he was living and working near the village of Llanddewi Velfrey. One night he was returning home from the village. He crossed a field by a public footpath, and was climbing over the stile to get onto the road when he encountered a phantom funeral (*Toili*) which happened to be passing by. It was a clear moonlit night, and Billy clearly saw the bier and coffin. He recognized most of the family mourners and some of those who followed in the procession. Afterwards he told a number of friends and neighbours about this strange experience. A few days later, this time in broad daylight, Billy was returning home along the same footpath and crossing the same stile, with exactly the same posture when he encountered a real funeral passing on the road. Afterwards his friends and neighbours were amazed by the way in which the real event matched exactly the details of what Billy had described to them a few days earlier.

Date: 1874   *Source: Meredith Morris p 94*

6.11 The Spectral Coffin

In the month of April 1975, Billy Thomas the postman was out walking in his garden near the village of Llanddewi Velfrey. It was quite late and very dark, but it was a beautiful starlit night and there was enough light for Billy to see where he was going. He had some family trouble on his mind, and he was deep in thought. At last he decided that he should return to the house, and as he turned he saw a man immediately in front of him on top of the hedge. The man appeared to have a strange wooden object beside him. He stood for a moment on the hedge bank as if he was resting, and then he picked the wooden object up and placed it on his shoulder. Then he came down off the hedge, and crossed the garden by an old public footpath which was still used by some of the older local people. As Billy watched the man continued along the path, crossed over a stile on the other side of the garden, and disappeared. Before he vanished from sight Billy realized that the wooden object was a small white coffin.

A few days later a small child in a neighbouring family sickened very suddenly with epilepsy, and died. Strange to say the carpenter from Llanddewi Velfrey brought the coffin to the house along exactly the same footpath, resting on the hedge-bank for a moment, crossing the garden and then climbing over the stile on the opposite hedge. Billy happened to be in the garden at the time. Every movement made by the carpenter was identical to that observed by Billy in his strange vision. The only difference was that on this occasion Billy exchanged a few words with the carpenter before he went on his way.

Date: 1875   *Source: Meredith Morris p 94*

6.12 Accident at Cold Blow

A well known squire who lived close to Tenby was travelling home by coach from the railway station at Narberth. He had been away from home for some time, and he had been met at the station by his coachman and his carriage and horses. The coachman was accompanied by a friend who sat with him in the driving seat, while the squire sat alone inside the coach.

As the coach and horses went along the road close to the hamlet of Cold Blow the coachman and his friend saw something which they described as a "black mass" moving towards them. It was a very dark evening, and the shapes ahead of them were very indistinct. But as they came closer they perceived that they were looking at a funeral. The horses became restless and then they were struck by panic, plunging and rearing and soon becoming uncontrollable. In the pandemonium the carriage was overturned, and the horses escaped from their harnesses and bolted into the distance. The coachman and his friend were thrown over a hedge into an adjacent field, from which they later emerged bruised and battered and covered with mud. The squire who was inside the overturned coach was shaken but not otherwise injured.

The three men were convinced that they had seen a phantom funeral, and certainly the behaviour of the horses had been quite out of character, for they were not normally frightened by crowds of people passing close to them. The squire later ascertained that there had been no funeral passing along the road on that date or at that time. The three were greatly shaken by their experience, but were afraid that they would encounter disbelief and even derision if they told the story to anyone else. They agreed on a mundane explanation of the accident, and it was only after the passage of a number of years that they admitted what had really happened on that dark evening at Cold Blow.

Date: c 1870   *Source: Curtis p 217*

6.13 Whistling with the Devil

One of the oldest of Pembrokeshire's superstitions is concerned with whistling. For example, it was always considered unlucky in Pembrokeshire for a young woman to whistle and many people believed that whistling was a means of talking with the devil.

Many years ago the Pembrokeshire antiquarian Ferrar Fenton was walking along on the pier at Fishguard in the company of a young sea captain. It was a pleasant evening, and all was well with the world, and Mr Fenton began to whistle contentedly as he strolled along. The captain immediately became greatly purturbed, and at last said to Mr Fenton "I wish you would not whistle here!" Mr Fenton was somewhat mystified by this, and replied "Why? What harm does it do?" The young sea captain lowered his voice and looked around him furtively. "Well you know," he said slowly, as if he was embarrassed at what he was saying, "We Welshmen and sailors are very superstitious about certain things, and whistling as you are now, is one of them."

Ferrar Fenton was intrigued by this and exclaimed that he could hardly believe that the young man would persist in believing old superstitions that belonged to generations long gone. The young man explained. "You see, my mother and all the old people of this town told me when I was a boy that your kind of whistling was the way in which the *Dyn hysbys* or magician used to talk with the devil, and sailors also believed something similar. It always makes my heart jump when I hear such whistling, especially when I am on dry land."

Suddenly the young captain pointed out to sea. "Look how muggy and hazy it is out beyond Pen Caer. You'll bring a gale, that's for sure, and I have to feel pity for the sailors who are afloat today when the sou'wester begins to rage in the Channel between here and Ireland."

Ferrar Fenton did not record in his diary whether a south-westerly gale really did blow up, but he explained that he had encountered on many other occasions a belief that sailors could make a direct invocation to "the Prince of Darkness" by whistling for the wind.

Date: c. 1890   *Source: Davies p 218*

6.14 Phantom Funeral at Eglwyscummin

It was harvest time in 1826. The wheat had ripened nicely and the farmers of the parish of Eglwyscummin were hard at work with their scythes and sickles in the corn-fields. The sun was high in the sky and the light was clear and bright. Around midday a group of farm labourers who were working in a field near Eglwyscummin church saw a funeral procession coming along the path. As it came closer they decided to stop work as a mark of respect, and they lay on the ground to watch the mourners going by. They recognised a number of local citizens, and at the end of the procession they saw an old woman dressed in mourning clothes, carrying a little bunch of flowers and foliage wrapped in a handkerchief. Clearly this was intended to be put on the grave. The procession went by and then disappeared as it approached the church, and the men realised that they had seen a phantom funeral.

Soon afterwards a local inhabitant died. The funeral procession went along the same path, with the same people as mourners, and with all the other details exactly as the farm labourers had described. Even the old woman with the flowers and the foliage wrapped in a handkerchief was there, taking up the end of the procession. This event made a profound impression on those who had seen the phantom funeral, for such things were rarely observed in high summer and in the midday sun.

Date: 1826   *Source: Curtis p 217*

6.15 The Phantom Funeral of Griffith Pencnwc

In the middle part of the last century William Havard owned a small shop in Newport and lived at a cottage called Penybanc. One night, having had various jobs to do after closing the shop, he was returning home very late. As he walked along East Street in Newport he was surprised to hear the sounds of wailing and weeping ahead of him. He stopped and listened, and suddenly he felt himself pushed backwards, as if by a large crowd of people. He could do nothing about it, but he was pushed along and jostled about until he came to a wider part of the road. There the crush became less intense, and he was able to extricate himself from the "phantom crowd". He pressed himself against the hedge at the side of the road and became aware of a *Toili* or phantom funeral procession going past him. He saw the coffin, recognized most of the mourners, and heard the women sobbing. What is more, he saw and recognized the local minister; and then he was even more surprised to see himself in the procession.

Much shaken by this experience, William hurried home and told his wife and two or three of his neighbours about it. Exactly a fortnight later, a man called Owen Griffith of Pencnwc died, and the funeral procession had a long walk into town. The mourners walked down Berry Hill, over the old bridge at Pen-y-bont and into the town. As the procession passed along East Street it was identical in every respect to that observed a fortnight earlier by William Havard.

Date: c 1860   *Source: Meredith Morris p 85*

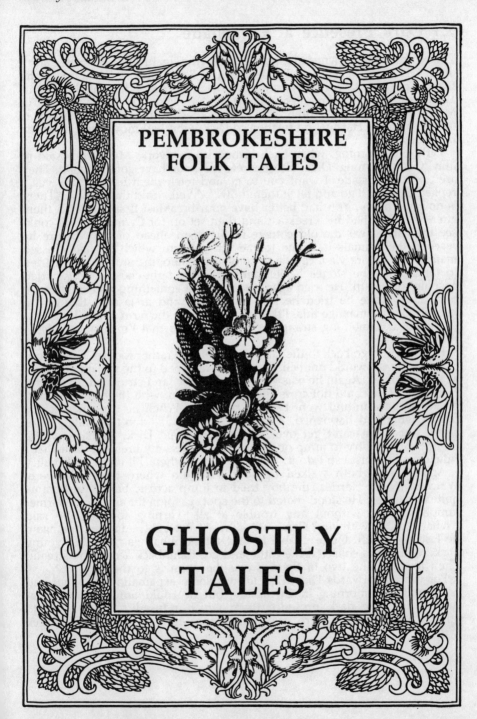

PEMBROKESHIRE
FOLK TALES

GHOSTLY
TALES

7.1 Dark Presence at Cwmslade

The old cottage of Cwmslade, near Castlebythe, featured in a strange story of an Old Black Witch (see **Pembrokeshire Folk Tales**, p 84). One of the two people who saw the apparition was Dick Harries, who was then about 12 years old. Two years later, when Dick left school, he went to work at Morfil, a big farm of the other side of the valley. At that time the farm was owned by a Mr Harries, no relation to Dick, who had moved into the area from England.

Early one morning, when Dick turned up for work, Mr Harries said to him "Good morning, Dick. Those wretched cattle have got out again. They are up in Cwmslade. I want you to go and fetch them back." "Yes yes," replied Dick. "I'll go and fetch them now." "Well," said the farmer. "There is no great hurry. You had better have your breakfast first and fetch them after." So Dick had his breakfast and then set off for Cwmslade. He could see the cattle near the old cottage in the cwm ahead of him. Before he reached the animals he came to the little stream which he had crossed many times before via a couple of convenient stepping stones. As he tried to jump onto the stones he suddenly became tight-chested and started gasping for breath. He tried again, but felt that something was smothering him. Every time he tried he lost his breath, and at last he thought to himself "I can't manage this. I'd better go back to the farm and tell the boss that there is something strange at the stream, so that I'm unable to fetch the cattle."

He turned to go back to the farm, but then felt rather foolish. Convinced that Mr Harries would not believe him, he returned to the stream and tried again to cross it. Again he was seized with panic, and struggled for breath. Furious that he could not cross such a tiny stream, with the cattle so close, he at last gave in and went back to the farm. When he explained to the farmer what had happened, Mr Harries said "Oh, don't be silly." "I'm sorry, but I just can't get over the stream!" said Dick. "What's wrong then?" "When I try to jump onto the stones I lose my breath." "But that's ridiculous!" "I just can't do it." "Oh, very well then. I'll come with you."

And so they both walked up to the stream where the cattle were. Watched by Mr Harries, the boy tried to jump across, but again became quite breathless. He stood rooted to the spot, gasping for air. So the farmer jumped across, without any trouble at all. Turning to Dick, he said "What's wrong with you? Come on -- jump!" The lad tried again, but again he lost his breath. Quite unable to understand what was affecting young Dick, Mr Harries collected the cattle and got them back across the stream. Then together the two of them drove the animals to the farm.

For years afterwards Dick tried to find some explanation for what had happened that morning in Cwmslade; but he could only conclude that there was some dark presence there which refused to allow him to approach the cottage where, two years before, he had seen the Old Black Witch.

Date: 1945   *Source: Gwyndaf 1990*

7.2 The Restless Corpse at Llangwm

Inside Llangwm parish church there is an effigy of a crusader, clad in full armour and with a sword in his hand. The face is handsome and expressive, and the head rests upon a plumed helmet. The thong of the boot (or is it the tail of a lion?), twined around one leg, bears some resemblance to a serpent; and this gives a clue to the identity of the person portrayed in stone. According to tradition, the crusader was the first De la Roche (called by the locals "Dolly Rotch"), the builder of Roch Castle who died from the bite of a viper. (See **Pembrokeshire Folk Tales**, 5.9).

Adam De la Roche (if indeed it is he who lies entombed) was a feudal lord who controlled large tracts of country in the old hundred of Rhos. The family had extensive estates in the Llangwm and Benton area, and it was they who built the church. There is an old legend that when Adam died he was buried in Roch Churchyard, not far from the castle gate. Next morning, it was discovered that the grave was open and the coffin gone, and a message eventually arrived that it had been discovered in the porch of Llangwm Church, twelve miles away. Servants were sent to bring the body back. This they did, and the coffin was re-interred at Roch. Next night the same thing happened, and the servants had to fetch the coffin back again. This happened on two more occasions, causing the servants and family to suspect that some supernatural forces were at work. So they determined to sit in the Churchyard and watch the grave throughout the night. As they sat there in the darkness, and as the midnight hour struck, they were amazed to see "a multitude of dwarfs and flying serpents" in the air. Transfixed with fear, they watched, helpless, as the phantom visitors dug down into the grave, lifted up the coffin, and flew off with it in the direction of Llangwm.

After this, it was agreed by all that the spirits would not let the cowardly Adam rest at Roch; and so the coffin was buried in Llangwm Church, where it remained undisturbed. Greatly relieved, the family eventually erected a monument over the tomb, complete with symbols relating to his life and death.

Date: c 1130   *Sources: Rogers Rees p 121, Timmins p 182*

7.3 The Ghost of John Paul Jones

John Paul Jones was a Scot who became a famous pirate in the latter part of the Eighteenth Century. He was an excellent seaman with little respect for the law, and after throwing in his lot with the Americans he was a considerable thorn in the flesh to the Excise men of England and Wales. According to legend, whenever he was operating around the western coasts of Britain, he would come in to the island of Caldey for water and supplies; and indeed Paul Jones's Bay is named after him. During the 1700s there were many rumours that local people helped the pirate in his irregular activities, and a tradition has survived that when he died in 1792 he was buried on Caldey, with his body being pushed into a crevice in the rocks near Small Ord Point.

It is still claimed on the island that the ghosts of John Paul Jones and his fellow pirates can be heard and seen burying treasure on his favourite beach. Sometimes there are strange bumps in the night, and the sounds of large stones being moved about. One encounter with the ghostly pirate band occurred in the early 1920s when Miss Rene Haynes was undertaking "psychical research" on Caldey. It was a calm and quiet evening, and Miss Haynes was sitting on the terrace of the house called Ty Gwyn. She could see the last embers of the sunset in the West, and the twinkling lights of Tenby on the mainland. She could hear no sounds but the mild splash of the waves on the ebb tide. There were a few voices chatting inside the house. The monastery was dark and there were no lights on in the Caldey settlement, but it was already too dark to dig without a lantern.

Suddenly Miss Haynes heard, with great clarity, something which was quite unexpected, namely the sound of iron spades digging down through sand and pebbles and occasionally striking rock. The sound went on for some time, indicating that the diggers were involved in a substantial task. Miss Haynes was not at all frightened by the ghostly digging, and a few days had passed before she recalled the legend of John Paul Jones and the buried treasure. On a calm night there is no doubt that the sound of digging in Paul Jones' Bay could be heard quite clearly in the settlement only 500 yards away, so there is no reason to disbelieve Miss Haynes's testimony.

Date: c 1922   *Source: Howells 1984, p 141*

At one time there were eight tall stones embedded in the ground......

7.4 The Field of the Dead

Not far from Llanychaer, on the slopes leading down to the Gwaun Valley, there is a place called Parc y Meirw, or "The Field of the Dead." It is a spooky place, and it is said that there was once a terrible, bloody battle here between the armies of two Welsh princes. Some people believe this to be the site of the Battle of Mynydd Carn, which took place in the year 1081 and which led to the establishment of two great dynasties: the dynasty of Gruffydd ap Cynan in Gwynedd and the dynasty of Rhys ap Tewdwr in Deheubarth. This particular battle is more likely to have taken place on Mynydd Morfil (see **Pembrokeshire Folk Tales**, stories 7.10 and 7.11); but whatever the truth of the matter it appears that the field was used as the burial place for hundreds of dead warriors and their horses.

Along the edge of the field there are the remains of the largest stone alignment in Wales. At one time there were eight tall stones embedded in the ground; the shortest was five feet in height, and the tallest twelve feet. According to legend, the stones were erected to commemorate the fallen soldiers. Now four of the stones have fallen over and the rest are embedded in a hedge bank.

Local people are still very reluctant to walk past Parc y Meirw after dark, and some prefer to make a long detour of a mile or more even during daylight hours. It is said that a "white lady" haunts the field on dark nights, always following a certain invisible trackway. White ladies tend to be relatively harmless; but there is also a darker legend associated with the site, and in the 1800's it was believed that there was a "prehistoric hobgoblin" at Parc y Meirw, who had the power to kill any person who trespassed on the haunted ground after dark.

Date: c 1050?   *Sources: Miles p 63, Brinton and Worsley p 37*

7.5 Hiraeth at Bettws Ifan

In the parish of Bettws Ifan, not far from Cenarth, there used to be a house called Penrallt Fach. Around the year 1883 it was occupied by a tailor called Samuel Thomas and his wife. One morning, very early, Samuel was woken up by a heavy knocking at the bedroom door. He asked "Who's there?" but received no reply, and everything went quiet again. The next morning, again very early, he heard a heavy knocking at the front door. It was so persistent that at last he got out of bed, calling out "All right, I'm coming. I'm getting out of bed now." He went downstairs, opened the door, and was surprised to discover that there was not a soul to be seen anywhere. He was somewhat perplexed about this, and made a note in his diary as to the date. After this, he was not troubled by the phantom knocking for some time.

Then, a year to the day later, in the first week of January 1883, Samuel's brother came to visit him. The two men went out shooting during the day, and in the evening Samuel went into his tailors workshop to do some work on a suit. Suddenly he heard two sharp knocks on the window. He went to the window and looked outside, but there was nobody to be seen. Then the knocking resumed, and went on for about ten minutes. On the second night the knocking started at about ten o'clock and continued until eight o'clock the next morning. On the third night the knocking resumed on the same window, and Samuel and his brother decided to try and discover what was going on. But every time they looked at the window or went outside to investigate, the knocking stopped; and every time they turned their attention to other matters, it resumed again. Several other young men from the neighbourhood came to investigate. They all heard the knocking, and all were equally mystified.

Now the word had got around the community that there was a "spirit knocking" at Penrallt Fach. On the fourth night some of the older neighbours came along, including the farmer who was Samuel's landlord. They all heard the knocking, and all became convinced that there was something supernatural about it. On the fifth night a very loud knock was heard on the front door of the house, as if somebody had charged at the door and was trying to break it down. On the sixth evening Samuel went out for a walk and was scared out of his wits by a tremendous noise which he described as the sound of "two hundred horses rushing towards him". By now Samuel and his wife were getting thoroughly frightened. On the seventh night there was more knocking, and when the knocking continued on the eighth night the tailor went out with his gun to threaten whoever or whatever was causing the disturbance. However, outside he heard a dreadful groaning voice in the air, and then a doleful wailing sound the like of which he had never heard before. Certain that he was hearing the terrible *Gwrach y Rhybyn*, he ran inside and locked the door.

After this, there was no more knocking or wailing, and life at Penrallt Fach returned to normal. However, some years later a Mr Lloyd from Newcastle Emlyn called at the house. He related that at the precise time of the "spirit knockings" he had been in America, at the bedside of an old woman who had once lived at Penrallt Fach. Her husband had died in the house, and she had emigrated to America with her family shortly afterwards. She was close to death, and when she realised that she could not return home to Bettws Ifan to die she was inconsolable, crying and moaning in her delirium as she slipped away over the course of a week or more. Mr Lloyd had been at her bedside when she died, after a final and heart-rending cry of "hiraeth" or longing after her old family home in Wales. This final act in the old lady's struggle against death coincided exactly in time with the wailing and groaning which concluded the strange events experienced by Samuel Thomas at Penrallt Fach.

Date: 1883   *Source: Davies p 211*

7.6 Waiting for Arawn

In the Celtic hero legends Arawn is the King of the Otherworld who changes places with Pwyll, Prince of Dyfed, in one of the famous stories of the Mabinogion. That particular story, related as Tale 2.1 in **Pembrokeshire Folk Tales**, has as its focal point the deep wooded valley of Glyn Cych. It may be that in the Celtic mind the valley was considered to be a magical place where the gods and the heroes of the past came into contact with one another, just as they did at the magical mound at Narberth.

There is a strange story from a wealthy farmhouse not far from Abercych, which again seems to emphasise a link with the Otherworld. A large and respectable family lived in the farmhouse, and space was at a premium. However none of the family would use a certain upstairs room because it was haunted by a "troublesome spirit" which could often be heard crying out (in Welsh) in a loud voice "Long is the day, and long is the night, and long is waiting for Arawn". The family used the room as an occasional guest bedroom, but the family members were so frightened by its haunted atmosphere that they hardly dared to open the door and go inside, even in broad daylight.

One cold winter evening the members of the family were sitting around the fire waiting for their supper when a stranger knocked at the door of the house. He was welcomed inside and encouraged to come and warm himself by the fire. This he did, and he asked hesitantly if he could be given some food and a bed for the night. The farmer readily agreed to share supper with him, but explained that they could not offer him a bed since they had hardly enough beds for themselves and since every bedroom was occupied. "We have one other upstairs room," said the farmer. "But we are afraid that it is haunted by a most miserable ghost, and we don't dare to ask you to spend the night there."

At this the stranger looked not at all surprised, but begged to be allowed to sleep in the room. He said that he was sure that there was nothing in the room which could do him harm. "Very well," said the farmer reluctantly. "You are welcome to sleep there if you insist, although I certainly would not sleep there myself. We will make a bed up for you after supper." During supper the stranger appeared very tired and participated only reluctantly in the family's conversation. At last someone asked him his name and the family was amazed when he replied "Arawn", for that was the name of the King of the Otherworld and the name which was always called out in the haunted bedroom.

The farmer's wife made up the bed in the haunted room, and the stranger retired for the night. Strange to say there were no sounds from the room; nothing moved and no cries echoed around the house. When the family got up the next morning the farmer went up to the guest bedroom to call the stranger for breakfast and to enquire whether he had passed a comfortable night. Much to his surprise there was no trace of the man. Furthermore the ghost was also gone, and from that day on the room was never again haunted or felt to be unpleasant in any way.

Date: c 1850   *Source: Davies p 160*

7.7 The Ghost of Pennoyre Watkins

Around 1780 Laugharne Castle and its estate came into the possession of one Pennoyre Watkins, under mysterious circumstances. Some say that he simply bought it, together with the Broadway Mansion estate, from the widow of Howell Gwynne.

Others say that Howell Gwynne (who lived near Brecon) got into financial difficulties and borrowed money from Pennoyre which he was unable to repay. The loan was secured on the estate. Gwynne also owed money to "certain parties in London." They sent officers all the way to Laugharne to recover their debts, but Pennoyre saw them coming and managed to prevent them from entering either the castle or Broadway Mansion. Unable to deliver their summons, the officers returned to London. Later all the deeds of the estate went missing, and Pennoyre demanded the repayment of his loan. Howell Gwynne would not or could not oblige, and when Pennoyre refused to wait the courts made over the castle, mansion and estate to him.

According to legend, the deeds of the whole estate were later found under the floor-boards of an upstairs room at Broadway Mansion when it was being demolished. According to another legend, the ghost of a former lady of Broadway Mansion often appeared in the house, and before the demolition work started she showed a servant the spot above the fireplace in the kitchen where the deeds, together with a quantity of money, were hidden.

Pennoyre Watkins was not fond of Broadway, and preferred to live in the castle, part of which was still habitable. On the demolition of the old mansion he used the stone and some of the timbers in the building of two large houses opposite the Great House in Laugharne, in a further house in King Street (later to become the Vicarage) and in a new mansion on Sir John's Hill. However, he died before his new mansion was finished.

After his death, the ghost of Pennoyre Watkins appeared frequently in the grounds of the castle and on Sir John's Hill. The servants saw him frequently in both places, but he appeared most commonly to an old woman who came from Pembrokeshire to live in the town. As a recent arrival, she had never met Pennoyre while he was alive or seen any picture of him. The servants would see her going to the castle ruins at midnight, where she would meet the ghost. One night the servants were astonished

Later all the deeds of the estate went missing, and Pennoyre demanded the repayment of his loan.

to see the ghost carry the old woman out of the castle and up Sir John's Hill. There was so much gossip about the old woman and the ghost that the Watkins family at last became very irritated. They decided to confront her and to seek the truth, and invited her to come to the Vicarage for a meeting.

When pressed, the old woman did not deny that she met and talked with "someone" in the grounds of the castle. But she was reluctant to divulge the name of the ghost. So the family decided to conduct an experiment. They asked the old woman into another room where a collection of portraits was hung. None of the portraits was named, and all of them were turned so that their faces were against the wall. One by one the portraits were turned and presented to the woman, and she was asked if she recognized the face. Always she replied "No". But then the portrait of Pennoyre Watkins was turned round, and immediately the old woman said "Yes! Yes! That is the man!"

The members of the family were amazed, because the old woman had neither met the old man when he was alive nor had any opportunity to see his portrait in the Vicarage. She was sent on her way, but the incident caused quite a stir in the town. One of the servants at the time was the aunt of Tom Owen the Town Crier; Tom heard the story from her when he was a child, and he passed it on to the writer Mary Curtis before he died in 1865.

Date: c 1810   *Source: Curtis p 73, p 135*

7.8 The Ghost of Caesar Mathias

At Little Milford there is an old house down by the tidal Western Cleddau which has had its own resident ghost for many years. The ghost is reputed to be that of Caesar Mathias, who was a well-known pillar of the local establishment. In 1753 he obtained a long lease on the Little Milford estate, and later moved into the house with his wife Alice. He lived there with his family until about 1779, and since he filled prestigious posts (for example, he was both Mayor of Pembroke and High Sheriff of the county) the house was very much a part of the social scene for the Pembrokeshire gentry. He died in 1795.

In the 1800s the house was used as a rectory, and it was said to be haunted by the ghost of the old gentleman. Near the front door of the house there was a curtain, behind which a set of stone steps led down into the cellar; the ghost used to come up the steps and emerge from behind the curtain, and it was firmly believed by the servants in the house that he lived in an underground passage that led from the cellar under the river to "the old palace" on the opposite shore near Boulston. The story was that Caesar had encountered and killed a smuggler in the tunnel long, long ago, and that his ghost could not leave the scene of this terrible and traumatic incident. Whatever the truth of the matter, when the Rev Jackson Taylor was living in the house as rector, the haunting was so bad that he could not keep any servants. At last he had to perform an exorcism, reading from the prayer book and going round the house with bell, book and candle. And just to make sure, he chased the ghost around the house with a horse-whip!

That apparently did the trick, and the haunting was much reduced; but later on, when the family of Mr Harcourt Roberts occupied the house after 1894, people were convinced that the ghost was still in the cellar. There were unaccountable sounds, such as strange creaking sounds and footsteps walking across the yard and then simply stopping. Pauline Roberts (now Burdon) spent her childhood at Little Milford, and was quite convinced of the presence of the ghost. She and her sister were too scared to go down into the cellar, but apparently their mother was not at all frightened by Caesar, and indeed quite enjoyed his company.

Date: c 1935   *Source: Mrs Pauline Burdon*

The story was that Caesar had encountered and killed a smuggler in the tunnel long, long ago........

7.9 Exorcism at Thorn Farm

Long, long ago the old farmhouse at Thorn, near Cresselly, was occupied by a widow and her family. The house was very disturbed by unearthly sounds, which could be heard every night in the same upstairs room. The sounds could be heard proceeding along the landing towards the top of the staircase, where they would fade away. Nobody could be induced to sleep in the haunted room, and indeed as the nights passed the haunting became so noisy that nobody in the house could get any sleep. At last the widow, her children and the servants were forced to leave the house each night and sleep in the barn across the yard.

The widow was desperate for help, so she called in to see the parish priest and explained everything to him. "Don't worry," he said. "I'll put everything alright." True to his word, he called at the farmhouse the same evening. He said he would stay in the farmhouse alone that night, in order to learn the nature and cause of the disturbance. So when everyone else had gone off to spend the night in the barn the parson was left alone. He prepared to settle down for the night, and armed with prayer-book, tallow candles and tinder-box he went upstairs and lay down, fully clothed, on one of the beds. He lit a candle and started to read aloud from his prayer-book. After about half an hour there was a loud crash downstairs, and he heard heavy, irregular, clumsy footsteps coming up the stairs. He kept on reading in a vain attempt to calm his nerves. Then he heard heavy breathing and he knew there was something in the room with him. He looked up and there stood a large lean horse! "In the name of the Lord," said the parson, in as loud a voice as he could manage, "What have I to do with thee? Away hence!" And with that the horse reared up, turned and vanished.

The parson was greatly relieved, but before he had a·chance to feel too self-satisfied there were more noises downstairs. More footsteps came up the stairs, this time brisker and lighter. The parson kept on reading out loud from the prayer-book. He heard a snort from the side of the bed, and on looking up he saw that a shaggy-haired bullock had entered the room. He repeated the same words, and the bullock disappeared. An hour elapsed, and the priest thought that everything was finished. He began to doze off, but sat bolt upright when there was an almighty crash downstairs, followed by the loudest and most fearsome noises he had ever heard. He thought that every room in the house must be filled with phantoms rushing about in terror. His hair stood on end as he wondered what might happen next.

Then he heard lighter, almost human, footsteps coming up the stairs. He kept on reading aloud from his prayer book. From the corner of his eye he saw the bedroom door open, and there stood a strange-looking little man, beautifully dressed in gold apparel, with rings on his fingers and jewellery around his neck. He made a polite bow to the priest, who said "Good evening, sir. Kindly take a seat." The little man sat on the corner of the bed. "In the name of the Lord, speak!" said the priest. And then the elegant phantom said "Why did they not ask me to speak before? I have come from the land of spirits, and I have paid these people many visits, but they have never had the courtesy to speak to me or ask me my business. Had they shown better manners, it would have been to their advantage, and I would have ceased to trouble them long since. Now I want you, sir, to carry out the few but important instructions that I am about to give you. If you don't, woe betide you. If you do, neither you nor they will ever see me again." The parson nodded and confirmed that he understood. The little man continued. "The instructions are these. An ancestor of the widow and her family left behind him a pile of money, and laid it in an earthen pot under the staircase. It is buried a full yard beneath the far left corner of the biggest flagstone. This fact you must convey to the family in the morning. They are the descendants of the old miser who buried the treasure, and they are the rightful inheritors of his estate. You are to instruct the widow to dig for the treasure herself, and to divide the money between herself and her children -- half to her and half to them. And you, merciful priest, for your trouble, are to take the grains of corn that will be found at the bottom of the pot, under the coins. These are my instructions. See that they are carried out to the letter, or in future I will give you much trouble."

After this curious speech, the little man said "Now I am going to leave you. Which way would you prefer me to depart, in sound, in fire, or in both?" "As you like," replied the priest. "Very well then," said the spirit, "I'll go in sound." He gave a deep bow, turned and went out of the room. The priest heard footsteps creaking down the stairs, and then he heard the front door bang as the spirit went outside. Then there was the most fearsome wailing, like all the demons in hell, followed by rolls of thunder, one after another, louder and louder until the noise was unbearable. The poor parson thought that his soul would be carried away on the waves of sound, and he cried out "Lord, have mercy on me!" And suddenly the noise stopped, and the priest realised that the only sound he could hear was the throbbing of his own heart.

That was the end of the disturbance, but the priest could not sleep. Exhausted and haggard after his experience, he watched and waited for signs of light in the dawn sky, and as soon as the first sun's rays touched the house he heaved a sigh of relief. He got up and went down to the barn to wake up the family, who had slept right through all the commotion. He called them to the hearth in the kitchen and recounted the whole story, passing on the strange speech of the spirit as exactly as he could. Then the widow went and fetched a shovel, and dug beneath the stairs. A full yard down she found the crock of gold. She put half on one side for herself, and gave the other half to the children. At the bottom of the crock there were some handfuls of grain, and these were given to the priest. Not a single grain was left in the crock. He put the grain in his pockets, and with the heartfelt thanks of the family he set off for home tired but elated.

The family became immensely wealthy, and bought lands and animals, fine clothes and fine furniture for the house, much to the astonishment of the neighbours. The parson did not fare badly either, for when he arrived home he found that the grains of corn in his pocket had been transformed; every one had been turned into a golden guinea.

Date: c 1750?   *Source: Meredith Morris p 39*

7.10 The Haunting at Molleston

In the year 1833 Jane Fortune lived with her parents at a cottage called The Pools at Molleston, near Narberth. An old couple called Ben and Betty Davies lived next door. Mr Fortune worked in the Pembroke Dockyard during the week and only came home at weekends. Normally he arrived home on a Saturday and returned to his lodgings in Pembroke Dock late on a Sunday evening.

One Monday morning in the middle of winter old Betty died in her sleep. She was buried on Wednesday. In the middle of the night after the funeral Jane heard a great commotion next door. She and the family wondered what could be the matter with old Ben. Early next morning the old man came into the Fortune's cottage and said that he had slept hardly at all because "something was dumbering" all night long. On Thursday night the noise was repeated, this time so loudly as to be almost unbearable. Neither Ben nor the Fortune family slept a wink, for all of them were terrified by the noise. Next day Ben confided to Mrs Fortune that he was worried about Betty's spirit coming back to haunt him. On Friday night the noise was even worse, and it was accompanied by the heart-rending cries of someone in great distress. Ben was so frightened that he called at the Fortune's house at the crack of dawn and said he could stand it no longer. He would have to leave his cottage.

Later that afternoon Mr Fortune came back from the Dockyard, and he was sad to hear of the death of his neighbour while he had been away. He was also told about the strange events which had occurred following the funeral. For a long time he thought in silence, and then he said that he would stay in Ben's house for the night to see if he could discover the cause of the problem. Ben was very grateful for this offer, and he was given a bed in the Fortune's house for the night. At bedtime Mr Fortune went next door to spend the night, with everybody listening intently. Sure enough, round about midnight the noises came; but they did not last for very long and after half an hour they faded away. Then Mr Fortune returned to his own house. He looked pale, and to Jane and the rest of the family he appeared numb and frightened by some experience which he would not talk about. In his hand he carried eight pence halfpenny in coppers. He handed the coins to his wife and told her that they had come from a hidden drawer in an old chest in the bedroom, and that they were to be handed to the Tea-man when he called on Monday morning. He said that Betty owed the money to the Tea-man from last week's visit.

When the Tea-man called at Molleston on Monday Mrs Fortune asked him if Betty owed him any money. "Oh yes," replied the Tea-man, "She owes me eight pence halfpenny from last week for a little bag of tea." Mrs Fortune paid over the coppers and the Tea-man went on his way. After that there was no more haunting of the house, for Betty's spirit was at peace after the payment of her debt. Jane and the rest of the family knew that Mr Fortune must have encountered her ghost and received instructions from it, for he could not possibly have known about the debt or about the hiding place that old Betty used for keeping her household coppers.

Date: 1833   *Source: Meredith Morris p 95*

7.11 The White Lady at Lamphey

In 1865 Jonathan Davies was a gardener at Lamphey Court. One night as
he was walking from the big house towards the village he saw a white lady
in front of him. This was somewhere near the old medieval palace used
centuries before by the bishops of St Davids. The lady was dressed in long
white robes, and she had an ethereal glow about her. Being a polite fellow,
Jonathan said "Good evening", and was disappointed to receive no reply.
She walked in front of him for some way and then suddenly disappeared.
Later on, as he walked back to the big house the white lady appeared again
at the same place. Again she walked in front of him, as if teasing him. By
now Jonathan had had a few pints at the local inn and he felt brave, so he
decided to give her a swipe with his walking stick. The stick went right
through her and he almost fell flat on his face; but then the white lady
became angry, and she danced about him wildly for several minutes,
making what Jonathan later referred to as "Satanic grimaces" which made
his hair stand on end. Then there was a flash of light and the white lady
disappeared. Jonathan never saw her again.

Date: 1865   *Source: Meredith Morris p 98*

7.12 The Three Spirits at Bowett

In 1855 Jonathan Davies, who worked at Lamphey Court, went off to
Bowett near Hundleton to see his girl-friend. He had heard that Bowett
was haunted by all sorts of evil spirits, but he had never seen or heard
anything of them himself. Later on, as he and his beloved were sitting in
the kitchen, they heard an almighty crash out in the hall, and pots and
pans started rattling everywhere. They went out to investigate, but there
was nothing to be seen. They sat down again in the kitchen, intent upon
continuing with their courting, but no sooner had they done so than they
heard an eerie groaning and moaning noise from the hall. They rushed
out, but again they found nothing. After this experience the couple
decided that the atmosphere was not quite right for courting, so Jonathan
took his leave and the girl went off to bed. As the young man came round
from the back door into the yard he saw quite distinctly three spirits flying
away from the house. He watched them as they travelled through the air,
and when they were some way off they suddenly disappeared in a cloud of
smoke. Jonathan never again visited Bowett after dark, and he maintained
to his dying day that the house was haunted. Indeed as late as 1900 the old
people of the neighbourhood used to refer to "strange sounds and strange
happenings" at Bowett.

Date: 1855   *Source: Meredith Morris p 99*

7.13 The Horrible Phantoms of Hoary Rock

On Kingston Hill near Pembroke there is a place called Hurry Rock or Hoary Rock. It had a reputation of being haunted, and local people used to speak of gatherings of ghosts who would sit together on the rock conversing and making mischief. Apparently the phantoms of Hoary Rock were a very belligerent bunch, for they would frequently chase passers-by and frighten the living daylights out of them. On one occasion they caught a gentleman who was travelling by on the road and threw him into Drustle Mill pond, and the poor man only just managed to escape drowning. The ghosts enjoyed this episode so much that they became even more horrible, and the people of the neighbourhood became so terrified that at last they consulted a witch. The witch was an expert at dealing with phantoms, and she travelled to Hoary Rock and banished them with a secret spell. After that the horrible phantoms were never seen again.

Date: c 1850   *Source: Meredith Morris p 101*

7.14 The Ghost at Cwm Meigan

At Cwm Meigan, not far from Boncath, there is an ancient sacred site which may originally have been a monastery established by the early Christian missionary St Meigan or Mawgan. Later the site was used by pilgrims as a resting place on their way to the shrine of St David's. In the Middle Ages it was an important trading centre, and there are records of an annual fair called Ffair Feigan. This was a centre of the Roman Catholic faith long after the Reformation, and the locals were accused of superstition and even idolatry by neighbouring protestants. There was a holy well near the old chapel, which gave forth three streams of water, one of which was said to heal warts, another sore eyes and the last heart disease. Cwm Meigan was also one of the great centres of the Ancient Game of Cnapan, and in Elizabethan times there were matches here between the men of Cemaes and the men of Emlyn which involved upwards of 2,000 players.

It is not surprising that a place so rich in history and religious associations should have its resident ghosts. One of these lives in an old house called Meigan Fare, now used as a delightful restaurant. When Debbie and Mike Newman arrived there in 1983 they very soon became aware of a shadowy presence keeping an eye on things. He is a young man dressed in a shirt with rolled up sleeves, a long waistcoat and trousers tucked into his boots. He has been seen many times by both the proprietors and their guests, and he was once spotted at the bar. He is not in the least threatening, and indeed appears to be uncommonly friendly. Research has revealed that his name is Tom, and that he was a farm-hand in the house who was tragically killed in a cycling accident about ninety years ago.

Date: 1993   *Source: local newspaper cutting*

7.15 The Mystery of Tremoillet

Not far from the old school at Pendine there used to be a mansion called Tremoillet. For many years it stood empty and in ruins before it was finally demolished, together with its out-houses and estate walls, in 1875.

In the old days there was a small stream here which ran across the roadway. An ancient legend was connected with the estate, to the effect that it would continue in the ownership of the Thomas family "for as long as the stream should flow". The stream was eventually diverted into a culvert, and for some years it seems to have dried up or gone underground into a subterranean limestone tunnel. At any rate, the last owner, Mr Zacharia Thomas, and all his family and servants were murdered one dark day under very mysterious circumstances, probably around the year 1600. The site of the old house is said to be haunted, and the writer Mary Curtis met several people who saw "a white lady" near the old Tremoillet pond, or where the stream used to cross the road, around the year 1870. Another respectable elderly gentleman who was travelling by pony trap from Marros to Pendine saw "the figure of a lady" standing near the dried-up stream bed.

Legends still persist about the slaughter of the Thomas family and their servants. It is said that when the house was finally demolished various skeletons were found, walled up or buried under the floors. The oldest story about the murders involves a notorious band of robbers from Greenbridge who terrorised the neighbourhood and who would stop at

...some say that the men and women of the community took matters into their own hands......

nothing in order to rob the wealthy of their valuables. Apparently they stripped Tremoillet of all its furniture, paintings, jewellery, fabrics and fittings.

However, the community had now had enough of the Greenbridge robbers. A sense of furious outrage at the murder of the Thomas family, and the plunder of Tremoillet Mansion, developed into a cool determination on the part of the community to rid themselves of the cancer in their midst. We do not know the details of what happened next; some say that the men and women of the community took matters into their own hands, and others say that the government of the day sent a force of law enforcement officers to deal with the robbers. But it appears that the members of the gang were pursued to a cave not far from Gilman Point, and there they were all killed in a very bloody battle. Afterwards the cave became known as Bloody Cave.

Date: c 1600   *Sources: Curtis p 307, Davies p 312*

7.16 Phantoms at Cresselly

Tom Phillips was a young man who lived at Cresswell Quay. In December 1842 he was courting a girl who lived near Loveston, and a friend of his was courting a girl from Thorn Farm, north of Cresselly. After spending the evening with their respective sweethearts the two lads were due to meet up at 1 am at Thorn Lane Cross so as to walk home together. Tom arrived at the cross in good time and since there was no sign of his friend he settled into the hedge to wait, deciding that he might be somewhat delayed. He was not in the least bit concerned, but after waiting for half an hour in the freezing cold he decided he could not wait any longer, and set out for home by himself.

He turned to set off along the Cresselly road, and was surprised to see a grey horse standing on the grass verge. He thought "What a spot of luck! I'll have a ride home to the Quay tonight." So he approached the horse, meaning to catch hold of its mane. The horse backed away. He made another approach, coaxing the horse gently, but again the animal backed away. So Tom made a rush at the horse; but this time it reared up and then took off, as if on hidden wings, and flew straight over a hedge nine feet high. Now that the horse had disappeared Tom began to feel frightened, for he could hardly believe his eyes. He walked quickly down the road, looking back frequently to see if the phantom horse was following him. It was not. Soon he was crossing Bishop's Bridge, but as soon as he reached the other side he heard a ringing and clanging of chains. He could see nothing, but the noise was terrific, and his hair stood on end. As he hurried on the noise travelled with him, and he soon reached old John Merriman's house. He thought of knocking on his door and asking for help; but since it was so late, and since he thought the old man would not believe his story, he decided to press on towards home.

Then the rattling chains stopped. Tom continued on his way, but after a few more yards he noticed on top of the hedge-bank a large earthenware pot with clusters of the most beautiful snowdrops he had ever seen. He

Tom reached The Shambles, shaking with fear, and sat in the hedge for quite a while as he composed himself......

was tempted to pick some of them, but they had a sort of ethereal quality, and he could not muster up the courage to try. Then the pot and the snowdrops disappeared. He continued to walk quickly and approached the main gate leading to Cresselly House. Opposite the entrance, right in the middle of the road, there was the most fearsome giant mastiff he had ever seen. He knew that there were no such dogs belonging to the big house, but there it was, menacing and vicious. Tom stood and the hound stood. Tom moved cautiously and the dog moved too. Tom sidled along the hedge, hoping to pass the dog, but it kept ahead of him, always the same distance away. Then, at the top of the hill, the dog disappeared into thin air. Tom reached The Shambles, shaking with fear, and sat in the hedge for quite a while as he composed himself and thought about which route to follow back to Cresswell Quay. Should he go through the village and knock up one of his friends? He thought he would only become a laughing-stock if he did, and so he decided to continue alone, taking the longer path via the Vicarage and The Grove rather than following the lane past the Norton, which was reputed to he haunted.

He passed the Vicarage and was opposite the entrance to The Grove when he suddenly saw in front of him a man with no head, with a long pole over his shoulder. As he watched in horror the ghost walked ahead of him, crossed over a hedge, then walked across a field, and disappeared over a hedge at the far side. Again Tom was terrified, and he ran the rest of the way back to the Quay. When he reached the culvert, he felt that at last he was safe.

Next day Tom went to see his sister-in-law Patty Phillips, who lived at The Back. She was older and wiser than him, and when he told her of his adventure she seemed not at all surprised. "Let that be a lesson to you, Tom," she said. "You've bin troubled by hobgoblins right enough. They was sent as a warnin' to you against goin' out courtin' at such hours on a Sunday night. Such things can only lead to mischief." After that, Tom never again went out courting on a Sunday evening, and never again walked the same route between Thorn Farm and Cresswell Quay........

Date: 1842   *Source: Meredith Morris p 91*

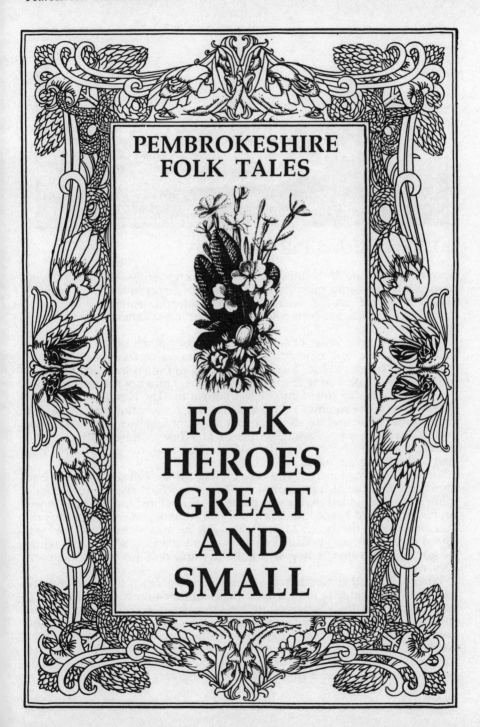

PEMBROKESHIRE
FOLK TALES

FOLK
HEROES
GREAT
AND
SMALL

8.1 Tom Birch's Tall Tales

Tom Birch was one of the most eccentric characters of Haverfordwest, who owned a tailor's shop near the bottom of High Street in the early years of this century. He ran the business with considerable enterprise and great good humour, assisted by a resourceful travelling salesman who was well known throughout Pembrokeshire.

Tom was a great teller of tall tales, and spent much of his time in his shop either inventing new and outrageous stories or recounting them to incredulous listeners. Tom loved the seaside, and often travelled to Broad Haven or Newgale during the summer months. Once upon a time, he told his cronies with due solemnity, he went down to "The Haven" for a swim. It was a very hot summer's day, and the water was calm and warm. He had a good swim, and decided that before swimming back to the shore he would have a rest by floating on his back. While in this position he fell asleep, and when he woke up he was amazed to discover that a sea-gull had laid an egg on his chest.

On another occasion Tom was on a cycling trip to Newgale. It was a fine summer's day, but as Tom looked out to sea he could see the rain clouds gathering. He decided that it was going to rain before long, so he jumped on his bicycle and headed for home. He looked back and could see the rain coming in over the beach at Newgale. But he was determined to keep ahead of the rain, and pedalled so quickly and travelled so fast that when he got home his front wheel was quite dry and only his back mudguard was wet.

When the weather was hot Tom enjoyed going down to the river bank near the New Bridge to eat his sandwiches at lunch-time. One day after a hard morning in the shop Tom ate his sandwiches and fell fast asleep in the sun. The tide had been low at the time. He did not know how long he had been asleep, but when he woke up he discovered that he was in Neyland. Honest to goodness, without a word of a lie, the tide had come up the river and picked him up, fast asleep. Then it had gone out again, carrying him down stream on the ebb all the way to Neyland.

Date: c 1910   *Sources: Richards p 12, Mr Jack Holt*

8.2 The Healer of Wiseman's Bridge

In the latter part of the Nineteenth Century a labourer called Thomas Prout was well known in the Wiseman's Bridge area as a curer of serious diseases which defeated the skills of local physicians. When healing adults, he insisted that the invalid undergoing treatment should never touch a drop of alcohol until the cure was complete. Apparently he knew if a patient had touched wine, beer or spirits during treatment and would abandon his cure forthwith if his instructions were disobeyed. But he had a special facility for curing children.

The Inn at Wiseman's Bridge was kept by a Mrs Hodge. Her young granddaughter was staying with her, and the old lady had undertaken to find a doctor who could heal the little girl. She was sadly afflicted with a strange disease of her eyes. They had a sort of film over them, and for sixteen weeks she complained that she could not bear the daylight. Every time she was exposed to bright light she screamed and closed her eyes tight, saying that the light caused a pain like pins and needles passing through her. In addition her lip was cut open in the middle and her nose was badly swollen. The poor little girl was quite exhausted, and for weeks she had been unable to sleep properly.

Having failed to find a doctor who could treat her granddaughter, Mrs Hodge at last asked Thomas Prout if he could help. He agreed and came over to the Inn to visit the girl. When he saw her he passed his hand over her face, gently touching it, and then he shook his hand down towards the ground as if he was shaking something off or throwing something away. He then said some strange words in a low voice, so quietly that no-one could understand what he said. This was done at 3 o'clock on a Friday afternoon, and the girl instantly went to sleep. She slept soundly for twenty-four hours, at which time Thomas Prout came back to the Inn and repeated the treatment. The little girl slept for a further twenty-four hours, but then when she awoke her grandmother was amazed to see that she appeared quite well. The film over her eyes had disappeared and only trifling marks of the disease were left on her face. When the writer Mary Curtis met the little girl some time afterwards, she found her in the best of health although there were some slight marks on her lip and around her eyes.

This was but one of many spectacular cures affected by the remarkable Thomas Prout, who otherwise lead an unremarkable life doing labouring jobs in and around the village. He would never tell his secret to anyone, claiming simply that he quoted from the Scriptures and healed through faith.

Date: c 1870   *Source: Curtis p 330*

8.3 How Shemi got the Cheese

Old James Wade (known as Shemi Wad in Welsh) was one of the best-loved local characters in the Fishguard and Goodwick area towards the end of the last century. He lived in a primitive clom cottage (with walls made of a mixture of clay, straw and rubble) in Broom Street in Goodwick.

Shemi's cottage was a favourite place with local children. The outside walls were covered in whitewash that had yellowed with age. Inside there were only two rooms, with a simple partition between them. There were earth floors and a tiny fireplace with an oven. In his "living room" he had two chairs and a table. In his bedroom there was a bunk bed with straw and chaff for a mattress, and a few dusty bits and pieces. One of his prize possessions was an ancient book entitled **Explanation to the Book of Revelation**; nobody was too sure whether he ever read it, but it had a battered leather cover on which he sharpened his cut-throat razor. The inside walls of the cottage were stained yellow and black as a result of years of tobacco spitting; Shemi chewed tobacco and had a great reputation for being able to spit about four yards with unerring accuracy.

Shemi wore wooden clogs on his feet, and dressed in an assortment of ancient clothes including a long jacket, baggy trousers, a waistcoat with only two buttons, and a woollen cravat. When he was going to Berea Chapel and had to be posh, he wore a long tail coat. On his head he invariably wore an old felt hat. The local children speculated that he never washed, and wore the same clothes, night and day, year in and year out.

Our hero was not too fastidious in matters of personal hygiene, and he was infested with fleas. He would go into "Siop Barsi" in the village to get his groceries. Next to the cheese counter there was a bench, placed there for the convenience of customers. When Shemi took a liking to a bit of cheese he would stand next to it or sit down on the bench, scratching himself ostentatiously. This was none too popular with the shopkeeper and the customers, all of whom had visions of a procession of fleas migrating from Shemi to the cheese. The shopkeeper would often give him a lump of the desired cheese just to get him out of the shop......

Date: c 1890   *Source: Gwyndaf 1990*

8.4 Shemi and the Beautiful Music

Shemi Wad used to do most of his serious drinking in the "Rose and Crown" and the "Hope and Anchor" in Goodwick, although sometimes he strayed further afield. He would hold court at the public bar, and when well lubricated he could be counted upon for a constant stream of stories.

A great number of fleas made their homes upon Shemi's person, and he was well acquainted with their habits. One of his favourite tales was the one about the flea and the match-stick, which he told over the years to hundreds of enthralled listeners.

"Well, Well! I never heard anything like it!" he would say. "There I was, fast asleep in my old bed and dreaming of the angels, when I was woken up by this beautiful singing. At first I thought I was in heaven. The night was quiet as the grave, not a breath of wind and not a drop of rain. I could hear this wonderful music going on and on. I couldn't understand where the singing was coming from. So I looked and I listened, and at last I was able to discover the singer. Do you know what it was, boys?" "No idea, Shemi! Tell us, where was the music coming from?"

"Well boys, without a word of a lie, cross my heart and hope to die, I had this little pot under the bed for putting my used-up match-sticks. At last I discovered that the sweet tune was coming from under the bed. So I lit my candle and took a look. There in the pot under the bed was a used match-stick, sticking up. And guess what? There, on the top of the match-stick, was an old flea singing in Welsh the beautiful hymn:

In the oceans and the waves,
There is no one to hold my head.

Very moving it was, I can tell you." And with that, having recalled the beauty of the moment, Shemi's breast would heave with emotion and he would wipe a tear or two from his eye. Then he would return to his quart of ale.

Date: c 1890   *Source: Gwyndaf 1990*

8.5 The Bleeding Charmer of Williamston

According to an old author, Little England Beyond Wales was, in the eighteenth century, the land of charms and charming. The custom of using charms for healing has continued in Pembrokeshire until quite recent times, and there are still many people who believe in the efficacy of certain incantations for the relief of pain and the cure of illness.

Jekky Arter of Williamston was a charmer who specialised in "stopping the blood". He was very well known all over Pembrokeshire. He had a magic wand which he would use only for certain cases. In the summer of 1839 a young man was pitching hay in a meadow adjoining the village of Cresselly. He was lifting up a very heavy "pick" of hay with his pitchfork, but as he did so he burst a blood vessel and collapsed in a pool of blood. Normally he would have died in a few minutes, but Jekky happened to be nearby. The other farm labourers shouted to him in a frenzy and he rushed over to see what the commotion was all about. On finding the young man on the ground Jekky immediately set to work. He dipped his finger in the young man's blood and signed him with a cross on his forehead. As he did this he muttered the following words from Ezekiel, Chapter 16, Verse 6: "And when I passed by thee, and saw thee polluted in thine own blood, I said unto thee when thou wast in thy blood, Live. Yea, I said unto thee when thou wast in thy blood, Live." He then stretched out his hand over the patient, as if in the act of blessing him. This process was repeated over and again until he had made the incantation nine times.

The bleeding stopped immediately, and the young man was taken away to rest and recover. The case caused a sensation in the Cresselly area, and was long remembered in the neighbourhood as a remarkable demonstration of Jekky's powers. When Jekky died around 1845 his skill died with him, and his magic wand was lost.

Date: 1839   _Source: Morris p 7_

8.6 The Charmer of Martletwy

Mr Jones the Charmer of Martletwy was very much a local hero in the area around his home village. He had received the gift of charming from his mother as she lay on her deathbed. By the time he died in 1905 he had charmed over one hundred patients with excellent results, and he never took any payment for his work. According to local people, whenever he became involved in healing a cure was "absolutely certain".

Once upon a time a local minister had a seven year old son who fell into the living room fire while playing at home. The child was terribly burned about the head; and the family were convinced that he would die. The doctor was called, and he rushed to the vicarage. However, when he had examined the little boy he decided that there was nothing he could do to save him. Talk of the accident reached the ears of Jones the Charmer, and immediately he made his way to the vicarage, for he and the vicar were old friends. The two men did not see eye to eye on everything, and the vicar often preached against charming, which was quite prevalent in the area at that time, referring to it as "the work of the devil".

When Mr Jones heard of the doctor's prognosis and when he saw the boy, he said "Let me charm the little boy. I know you don't believe in it, and that you have often preached against it, but never mind - if I don't cure him I will not have made matters worse. A drowning man will cling to a straw." The minister, with his mind wavering between despair and disbelief, at last agreed to his friend's request.

So the Charmer went into the boy's bedroom where he lay terribly ill on his bed, with his head covered with appalling burns. This is what Mr Jones said: "Three little angels came from the East to try their virtue on fire and frost. In fire! Out frost! In the name of the Father and of the Son, and of the Holy Ghost." As he spoke the formula he described a clockwise circle with the index finger of his right hand over the burnt area on the boy's head. This was done three times, with the Charmer repeating the formula each time. Then he breathed three times on the affected part.

With that, Mr Jones took his leave and set off for home, saying that the boy would be much better by tomorrow. The vicar and his wife hardly dared to believe it, for they knew the child to be close to death. But true enough, by next day the boy was much brighter, and the burns were partly healed. Mr Jones returned and repeated the charm, and he repeated it again on the two following days. Then, as he set off he said "That will do the trick. Now the boy will be completely better in a fortnight's time."

And so it was. After two weeks the boy was out playing with his friends, with all traces of the burn gone. Never again did the vicar preach about charms as the work of the devil.

Date: c 1890   *Source: Meredith Morris p 3*

8.7 The Waunbwll Bull

Thomas Phillips of Waunbwll was one of the great local characters of North Pembrokeshire in the early years of this century. He was a wealthy man whose appearance belied his skill as a farmer and his wisdom in matters of finance. He was famous for his Welsh Black cattle, which were well bred and well fed. The story of "Twm and the men from the Ministry" is told in the companion volume entitled **The Last Dragon.** This story is a variation on the same theme, from another source.

The largest animal in Twm's herd of cattle was a magnificent and very savage bull which he used to keep in a field just below the farmhouse at Waunbwll. A public footpath ran across this field, which was regularly used as a thoroughfare to a neighbouring farm. The animal was so bad tempered that no one dared to use the footpath, so the neighbours called to see Twm and pleaded with him to move the bull to another field. Twm, who appeared to have more enemies than friends, was clearly not on good terms with his neighbour, and refused to move the creature.

Frustrated and angry, the neighbour eventually threatened to take the matter to Court. "You do as you please," said Twm. "That's where the bull is, and that's where the bull stays." Some weeks later a policeman knocked on the front door at Waunbwll, carrying in his hand a Summons which he intended to hand to Twm. "Good morning, Twm," said the policeman. "I am here to hand you this Summons for stopping people from using the public footpath in your field." Twm refused to take the document. "It is nothing to do with me, Constable Jones Bach," he said. "I'm not stopping anybody from using the path. Go and give it to that bull down there, if he's the one that's causing the trouble." And with that he closed the front door, leaving the policeman spluttering and still holding the Summons in his hand. Naturally enough, the Court case was never heard, and the bull continued to graze peacefully in the meadow.

Date: c 1905   *Source: Mr Noel James*

8.8 Madame Bevan and the Burglar

It is difficult for those of us who live in the last decade of the twentieth century to realise that only 200 years ago people could be condemned to death, and hung on the gallows, for offences now considered to be quite petty. A sad story which reminds us of the harsh world of the 1700s comes from the little town of Laugharne.

Madame Bevan was one of the pioneers of the "Circulating Schools" movement in South Wales. The leading light in this movement was Rev Griffith Jones, the rector of Llanddowror, who brought simple education, and the ability to read the Bible, to many thousands of uneducated folk throughout Wales in the decades following 1730. It is calculated that by 1750 no fewer than 150,000 Welsh people of all ages had been taught to read. The success of the schools was due in no small measure to the financial and political support given to Rev Jones by Madame Bevan of Laugharne. As a wealthy and respected landowner she was able to smooth the path followed by his controversial movement in the face of great hostility from the church.

Madame Bevan lived in a handsome and substantial house close to the Town Hall in Laugharne. She was a good Christian lady, greatly loved by all her friends and neighbours, but she was careful with her wealth and the house was renowned as something of a fortress. The reputation of the house, and the wealth it contained, spread far beyond the confines of Laugharne, and it was said among the criminal classes that it was impossible to break into. Word of Madame Bevan's house reached the ears of a famous London burglar, and he was offered a wager that he could not break into it. He accepted the wager eagerly.

The burglar travelled to Laugharne, and after careful research he managed to break into the house and to steal a number of valuable items. He won his wager, and although he was not caught in the act of burglary, word of his exploit reached the ears of the constables, who managed to arrest him. He was brought to trial, but things did not go well for the forces of law and order, since there was very little evidence on which to convict the man. Madame Bevan reluctantly agreed to appear as a witness. The only incriminating item found in the possession of the burglar was a certain book, which had no name inside the front cover. The counsel for the prosecution questioned Madame Bevan persistently and aggressively about the ownership of this book; but she was extremely uncooperative, knowing that the burglar would be sent to the gallows if the ownership of the book could be proved. But while she had no wish to send a man to the gallows, neither could she lie, and she found her cross-examination almost impossible to bear. At last, tired and confused, she blurted out angrily "Well, if you will have it, look at page 59 and there you will find my name."

Sure enough, when the court officials opened the book at that page they found her name inscribed there. The case was proved and the burglar was convicted. The Law took its course and he was hanged on the gallows. For Madame Bevan, who tried to demonstrate the virtues of charity and forgiveness, this event was a terrible tragedy which stayed with her for the rest of her life.

Date: c 1760   *Source: Curtis p 145 & 166*

8.9 Mary Palmer Goes to Court

Mary Palmer was one of the famous Llangwm fisherwomen who were renowned throughout Pembrokeshire during the early years of this century. She belonged to a tough breed of women, born into large families, hardened by endless work and childbearing, expert in household management and as liberated as any of the feminists of today. The Llangwm women worked on the river and in the home; and they walked prodigious distances to the main towns of West Wales with their panniers and baskets laden with herrings, oysters and cockles. Sometimes they would walk more than 35 miles in a day, spending more than 8 hours on the road. With their colourful costumes and felt hats they were seen in all the main markets on a regular basis, haggling with customers but normally selling their catch for a few miserable pennies.

Mary was born in 1833 into a family of seven children. She had no proper childhood and hardly any education. By the age of twelve she was at work on the river. At the age of nineteen she married, and by 1852 she had produced nine children. She helped her husband John with his dredging and fishing, sold the catch at the local markets, helped to build a new cottage for the family, and contrived to manage the household and to provide a loving Christian family environment for her children. John died in 1888, leaving Mary a widow, and soon she was alone in the cottage as the last of the children married and flew away from the family nest. Mary survived until 1921, when she died at the ripe old age of 89, still as tough and garrulous as ever and still known by the affectionate and mischievous nickname of "Mary Hush".

In 1912 Mary became extremely famous, featuring not only in the pages of the local press but also photographed and interviewed for **The Daily Mirror**. The cause of this sudden celebrity status was a court case in the Shire Hall in Haverfordwest. By this time Mary was in receipt of the new-fangled Old Age Pension of five shillings per week, but life was still very hard, and she was greatly upset when the parish council levied a "special water rate" to pay for a new pump at the local reservoir. Mary contended that as far as she was concerned the old water supply had been perfectly satisfactory, and she did not intend to pay for a pump installed for the sake of a few privileged households. There were other protestors as well, but most of them paid up when summonses were issued.

Mary, together with Mrs Absalom James of Hook, duly appeared at the Shire Hall before the bench of local magistrates. Mrs James appeared first, and short-circuited the proceedings by asking for an adjournment, which was granted. Mary was called, and proceeded to hobble down the court steps, dressed in her traditional Llangwm costume complete with flannel shawl, white frilly cap and felt hat. She was leaning heavily on her stick. But before she reached the front of the court-room the Chairman of the bench adjourned her case as well.

Mary was somewhat non-plussed by all this, but then she saw Joe Davies, the assistant court overseer, out of the corner of her eye. She waved her stick at him and shouted "Joe! You will have to get a carriage to drive me home. I cannot stand, much less walk." The court-house was swept with a gale of laughter from public and officials alike. Mary became even more confused, and asked what was going on. She was told once more that her case was adjourned, upon which she again turned on the hapless assistant overseer. "You ought to be ashamed to bring me here, Joe!" she shouted. "How am I going home, gentlemen? I have been on the road since the dawning of the day because I could not rest. You bring me here, an old woman of 82 years of age, and been a widow for 24 years, and nursed a heavy family, gentlemen. Yes, to bring me here, you ought to be ashamed of yourself, Joe. I never paid a rate in my life."

By now the proceedings of the court had been reduced to the level of a Music Hall farce, and Mary was beginning to enjoy herself. Suddenly she recognized the Chief Constable, smiled broadly, jumped up and shook his hand heartily. "Well well. How nice to see you, Mr Summers!" she said. "How are you? I am so pleased to see you looking so well." Mr Summers was covered with embarrassment, but he was spared further indignity as Mary turned and walked slowly out of the court. As she went, with all eyes following her, she continued to complain in a loud voice that it was a shame to bring her to court, and that Joe would have to drive her home to Llangwm. As she disappeared along the corridor the last words to be heard were "Go and get the carriage to bring me home, Joe."

Outside the court-house Mary recognized the county Member of Parliament, Mr Roch. Not in the least over-awed by his status, or by the presence of the local press, she greeted him like an old friend and promptly invited him to tea. The county member graciously accepted the invitation.

Then Mary returned home, presumably in Joe's carriage, having totally destroyed the solemnity and discipline of the courtroom and having left the inhabitants of the public gallery in fits of hysterical laughter. It was not surprising that she never heard anything more of the summons or the special water rate. Nor was it surprising that she became, in her old age, a darling of the local journalists and even a **Daily Mirror** personality.

Date: 1912   *Source: Thomas p 12*

8.10 The Wild Man of Skokholm

The last man to farm on Skokholm was one Jack Edwards, always known to the Marloes people as "The Bulldog". He was aptly named, being short of build and possessing immense physical strength. In his youth he was in constant trouble on account of his short temper and his tendency to solve problems with his fists. But he was also widely read, and was one of those converted during the great religious revival of 1904-1905. During his stay on the island he kept a small herd of milking cows, over one hundred hens, four pigs and various horses and fat cattle. He grew some corn and root vegetables, and he always had a good hay harvest. He sold eggs and butter on the mainland every week, and also derived an income from the sale of livestock, rabbits, seabird eggs, lobsters and crayfish.

Bulldog Edwards had a reputation as a good farmer, but he was also a hard taskmaster. Various young men and women entered his service on the island, and he always insisted that he got value for money out of them. The little story of the Wild Man of Skokholm relates to one of his farm lads who worked on the island around the year 1908.

Edward Pearce had come to Pembrokeshire from "away" or "up the line". For one so young he appears to have been something of a character, and he was reputed to be quite fearless. During his time in Marloes he was greatly admired as the only person who had ever had the courage to pinch apples from the policeman's garden. He went to work for Bulldog Edwards on Skokholm, and for three years he remained there without once returning to the mainland. When he came back to civilisation he looked like the Wild Man of Borneo, with a thick beard and long hair falling down over his shoulders. His appearance caused great amusement until he was eventually prevailed upon to have a shave and a haircut.

Young Edward, having survived the rigours of life on Skokholm for three years without a break, had a huge appetite, and it was known that he had a passion for gulls' eggs. One evening in the village inn he was asked how many eggs he could consume at one sitting and he replied that thirty would be just about right. This remark was greeted with incredulity, and one of the regulars at the bar immediately issued him a challenge, claiming that he could not possibly eat thirty hard-boiled hens' eggs. "No problem at all," said young Edward. Warming to the challenge, Charlie Hooper said "If tha ca'st eat 'em, I'll pay for 'em." Jimmy Edwards the Shop was there at the time and he immediately went and fetched thirty eggs. These were duly hard-boiled, as more and more people crowded in to see the action.

Much to everybody's astonishment, Edward sat down and happily demolished all thirty hard-boiled hens' eggs. Years later, an old man who told the story to Roscoe Howells recalled "Well now, them eggs went down one after t'other, smooth as water off a goose's back. An' dost tha know, the young bugger only had to have salt with the last ten!"

Date: c 1910   *Source: Howells p 131*

8.11 Bill Frost's Aeroplane

Bill Frost was one of the great unsung heroes of Pembrokeshire, and he should probably have his name inscribed in the record books as the first man to achieve powered flight.

Bill was a carpenter by trade, and he lived in a cottage on St Bride's Hill in Saundersfoot. In later years he was the founder and conductor of the Saundersfoot Male Voice Choir, and he was also a deacon of Bethany Chapel. In his middle age he became fascinated by the idea of powered flight, and around 1890 he began to undertake experiments with propulsion systems, fuselage and wings. He designed a lightweight aircraft, made mostly of wood and probably with double wings. He built a power system based upon hydrogen fuel, and the engine drove a single propeller via a crankshaft. The hydrogen cylinder was built on to the top of the fuselage.

By 1895 Tom had completed the construction of his aeroplane; and in that year he took out a patent on the design. Then he undertook his first trial in a field near Saundersfoot. He strapped himself into the pilot's seat, started up the engine and began to roll forward. Then, to the amazement of the locals who were watching, the aircraft actually took off and started to rise higher and higher. Unfortunately the field was not a very large one, and Tom tried desperately to clear the hedge which was looming up, too close for comfort. His methods of controlling the aircraft were primitive to say the least, and he tried to steer clear. He was now a good thirty feet from the ground, but unfortunately the aircraft wing touched a tall tree and he had to make a crash landing in the next field.

Tom was exhilarated to have flown from one field to the next, and somewhat relieved to have escaped with his life. He determined to repair the damage next day, and to undertake another test flight. So he returned to his workshop, leaving the aeroplane where it was. Sadly, he omitted to fasten it securely to the ground. In the night a ferocious storm blew up, and when Tom anxiously returned to the field in the morning he discovered that the prototype had been carried into the air and smashed to pieces.

This calamity broke Bill Frost's heart, for he had neither the time nor the cash resources to build another aeroplane. He wrote to the Secretary of State for War, offering his patent to the nation. The Under-Secretary, Mr St John Broderick, wrote to thank Bill for his kind offer, but declined to accept. In his letter he wrote "The nation does not intend to adopt aerial navigation as a means of warfare."

And so died Bill Frost's wonderful project. His flight was not properly monitored or recorded; but he certainly took to the air eight years before the Wright Brothers made their famous flight in 1903 and fourteen years before Bleriot flew across the English Channel. Sadly, his name is not even recorded in the record books of aviation pioneers.

Date: 1895   *Source: Howells 1977, p 56*

8.12 The Flying Coffin

It was a cold and snowy winter, and Benchi was home on leave from the Battle of the Somme. He was a Welsh Guardsman, and he had seen The Grim Reaper stalking the trenches of the battlefield. His eyes had become accustomed to the sight of dead men, and his nose could endure the stink of corruption. Thus far Benchi had cheated death, but a bullet had cut a notch out of his right ear. Through the terrible days of the War he had kept sane by retaining his humour and developing a strong sense of the absurd, and these qualities stood him in good stead during the grotesque episode of the flying coffin.

Up in the most inaccessible part of the valley near Pen-y-bryn, in the parish of Bridell, there was a lonely cottage occupied by a bearded loud-mouthed peasant and his family. The man was frequently drunk, and during his drinking sessions he quarrelled violently with everybody and beat his wife and children. He eked out a living by hauling with his horse and cart, but during the winter of 1916-1917 the snow-drifts made work impossible, and he had ample time to hit the bottle and to abuse his wife. One day after a heavy drinking session he roared into the kitchen brandishing a butcher's knife. The mother called on her fifteen year old son for help, and a furious struggle ensued, as a consequence of which the father fell onto the knife and expired. The family called the doctor, who plodded through the snow to perform the post-mortem in the outhouse. At the coroner's inquest a verdict of death by misadventure was returned, and the coroner told the family that they were in no way to blame. He assured them that the full sympathy of the community was with them in their time of tragedy.

The family now had to organise a respectable burial. It so happened that Benchi's brother William was the local undertaker, and he was asked to make an oak coffin. William and Benchi had to face the problem of transporting the coffin through the snowy woods to the isolated cottage in the cwm. They set off through the snow-drifts with their younger brother and with young James Williams, who knew the woods like the back of his hand. A pony cart was used to transport the coffin to the end of the lane, but after that it had to be manhandled across three fields. At last the coffin party could see the cottage below them, nestling at the foot of a steep slope at the head of the narrow valley. It was full moon and it was so cold that the deep snow was frozen solid. The lads decided that it would be best to slide the coffin down the slope, and William removed the lid to get at his bag of tools and at the webbing straps with which they could control the descent. However, the coffin was very heavy, and suddenly Benchi, who was at the front end, shouted to young James "Jump in, the darn thing is on the move!". Without thinking Benchi fell backwards into the coffin and James jumped in as well, and the coffin shot off down the slope, leaving William and his young brother far behind with the lid and the bag of tools.

As the coffin gathered speed James found that he was the helmsman, and since he was wearing clogs he was able to do at least something to control the direction followed by the missile. Soon they were travelling at breakneck speed, feeling insanely exhilarated, laughing and yelling at the tops of their voices. Benchi shouted directions, and James did what he could to keep the missile on course. At the foot of the slope there was a

William and Benchi had to face the problem of transporting the coffin through the snowy woods to the isolated cottage in the cwm.

small gate about four feet wide. Luckily it was open, and James managed to steer the coffin through the gap without mishap and to negotiate a sharp bend outside the outhouse where the corpse lay. The high-speed travellers came to a halt against a hay-rick, following which both of them collapsed in fits of hysterical laughter. Twenty minutes passed before William and his little brother arrived, after which they too were overtaken by hysteria.

Disturbed by all the hilarity, the widow came to the door, at which point William and his colleagues were forced to adopt a demeanour more appropriate to the occasion. "Do what you like with him," said the widow. "I don't want to see him again, but when you have finished come in and have a cup of tea." So the lads took the coffin into the outhouse, intent upon the completion of their task. Unfortunately the corpse had not been laid out properly, and what with the freezing cold weather he refused to fit neatly into the coffin. His legs were bent, and the knees were several inches above the coffin top. This caused some discussion, but at last Benchi took decisive action by jumping onto the corpse's knees and bouncing up and down. Suddenly the legs straightened, but the corpse sat bolt upright in the coffin, bringing the sallow, bearded face of the dead man within an inch of Benchi's nose. "Damn it all man," said Benchi. "I don't fancy your cold kisses." Then, in a gentle voice which was full of compassion he added, as if he was addressing a little child, "The time for fooling about is past and you must now lie down and go to sleep." Gently they pressed the upper part of the torso down, and the lid was screwed on tightly, to the great relief of all concerned.

After all that the coffin party went inside for a cup of tea and a piece of bread and butter, and the lads agreed that never had a simple repast tasted so good. The coffin was later carried by relays of bearers to the local chapel, and a few days later the old reprobate who had brought a cruel fate upon himself was given a splendid and tearful funeral which would have done credit to even the most saintly member of the local community.

Date: 1917   *Source: Williams p 49*

8.13 Cyhelyn the Prophet

According to the old books, Cyhelyn was the grandson of Pwyll, Prince of Dyfed, one of the great heroes of **The Mabinogion**. As befits the grandson of a hero, he had special powers, and was known as Cyhelyn Fardd (Cyhelyn the Bard) or Cyhelyn the Prophet. He was the favourite bard of William Marshall, the Earl of Pembroke. He spent much of his time around the year 1200 in Pembroke Castle, and also accompanied the Earl on his military campaigns, where his powers as a prophet or *Cyfarwydd* came in very handy.

In the castle Cyhelyn had a bed in the corner of the bedroom occupied by the Earl and his wife, for William liked nothing better than a boring Welsh heroic tale to send him off to sleep. One evening the Earl and his wife were tucked up nicely in bed, beginning to nod off as Cyhelyn recounted in detail some old saga from **The Mabinogion**. The Earl's wife made a few fatuous comments about various things, which Cyhelyn disregarded. Suddenly, in the middle of the saga, Cyhelyn went into a trance and had a powerful vision. He said that he could see the corpse of a nobleman washed up on a certain beach in Milford Haven, and described him as dressed in gold-braided clothes, with a gold torc around his neck and fabulous gold rings on his fingers. Then, exhausted, Cyhelyn went in to a deep sleep. However, William and his wife had heard Cyhelyn's words, and very early in the morning William crept quietly out of bed, gathered a troop of soldiers, and went off to the beach to search for the nobleman's corpse. There they found it, just as Cyhelyn had described, and stripped it of all its treasures.

While they were away, Cyhelyn woke up, and was furious to discover that the Earl had risen early to go off treasure-hunting. In a fit of pique he gathered up his possessions and left Pembroke Castle to set off along the road to Narberth. When the Earl returned with his treasures and found that Cyhelyn had gone, a sense of guilt flooded over him for what he had done, and he sent out emissaries to find Cyhelyn and bring him back. One of the men found the prophet on the road and managed to convince him to return to Pembroke. When he arrived he rebuked William in a voice as dark as thunder, and to appease him the Earl offered him marriage to any one of his three daughters and any cantref in Pembrokeshire as her dowry. Cyhelyn may have been something of a mystic, but he was no fool, and he accepted the offer.

He chose his bride in a somewhat unusual way, by asking William if he could simply look at the girls as they lay fast asleep. By observing their postures he could tell their natures, and could also prophecy the fate of their descendants. He chose the daughter called Gwrangen as his wife, and the cantref of Cemaes as the dowry. At this, William was delighted, for Gwrangen was not the most beautiful of his daughters, and Cemaes was the poorest cantref in the Earldom. But Cyhelyn was happy; he married Gwrangen, who proved to be a wonderful wife and mother, and he became ruler of the most beautiful cantref in Wales. The couple moved to Nevern and made their home in the old castle, high above the wooded river valley once occupied by St Brynach and his monks.

Date: c 1200   *Source: Jones p 71*

8.14 Squire Owen's Feud

George Owen of Henllys, near Nevern, was one of Pembrokeshire's more colourful characters in the colourful reign of the first Queen Elizabeth. We know him best through his writings, and especially through the pages of his most famous book, **The Description of Pembrokeshire**. He was industrious, thrifty, ambitious and far-sighted, and in his book he gave full reign to his good humour and his acute powers of observation. His book, still widely used, is one of the most valuable and comprehensive records of social and economic life in Elizabethan Britain.

George was somewhat larger than life, and he was immersed in the social life of the Pembrokeshire gentry. He was obviously well loved, for he fathered at least 24 children; but he also had a great many enemies, for he allowed nothing to stand in his way as he tried to re-establish the glories of the old Barony of Cemaes and as he pressed his own claims to the title of Lord Marcher. He married well, into the family of the Philippses of Picton Castle, and the Owen and Philipps families formed a strong alliance in a long-standing feud with Sir John Perrot and his cronies. Sir John controlled Haverfordwest and much of South Pembrokeshire, but his influence was so powerful (and also corrupt) that many of the lesser gentry resisted him whenever they could. Both factions kept gangs of armed retainers, and occasionally their rivalry erupted into violent clashes.

One market day in the year 1572 George Owen and his faithful retainers rode down from the snowy Presely Hills into Haverfordwest. The squire expected trouble, for the Perrot faction also had a large group of armed men in town. After a number of ugly incidents around St Mary's Church (where the market stalls were set up) the Sheriff, who was one of Perrot's men, considered that a riot might erupt at any moment; and so he decided to arrest those most likely to incite violence. He arrested one Rees Awbrey, claiming that he was a trouble-maker, "by repute a card player, a frequenter of taverns and an associate of a thieving woman." Awbrey was clapped into the County Gaol. Then the Under-Sheriff tried to arrest Rees Gwyneth of Nevern, a one-eyed North Walian with a reputation for horse-stealing and even murder. However, Gwyneth was too smart for the posse, and he managed to escape to the High

Street house of an Owen supporter. The Sheriff's men broke down the front door and pursued the fugitive up the stairs; but at the top of the second flight they were confronted by William Philipps of Picton Castle, John Barlow of Slebech Hall, and George Owen of Henllys.

A furious row ensued, and tension mounted when the three gentlemen refused to hand over the one-eyed ruffian. By now there was a large crowd outside, some of them shouting for the Perrot gang and others for the opposition. The situation was brought under control only when the MP for the Town and County of Haverfordwest, Alban Stepney, rushed to the scene. He told the Sheriff's men that they had no right to arrest Gwyneth within the "liberties" of the town, and he sent them packing with their tails between their legs. He also told them to go and release Awbrey from the Gaol. The towm Mayor was summoned to the scene, and since he belonged to the anti-Perrot faction he was only too pleased to ship the Under-Sheriff off to Gaol himself for infringing the rights of the borough.

Things were now very confused indeed, but eventually both parties realised how serious the consequences would be if there was any bloodshed, and they agreed to an uneasy truce. Later that day, feeling that the Perrot faction had had the worst of the encounter, George Owen and his merry men, including Awbrey and Gwyneth, set off again through the snows of Presely back to Newport. However, all concerned were somewhat chastened by the episode, and the feud never again boiled over in quite the same way. Sir John Perrot was forced thereafter to behave with more diplomacy towards the other local gentry, but his power base in Haverfordwest was never again seriously threatened.

Date: 1572   *Sources: Miles p 105, James p 45*

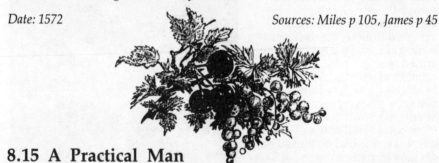

8.15 A Practical Man

In 1973 Mr Ivor John of Haverfordwest fell ill, and had to spend a short time in Withybush Hospital. In the next bed there was an old man who ran a little farm up in the Presely Hills. The two men spent a great deal of time chatting together, and one day the conversation turned to children and grand-children. Ivor mentioned that he had six grand-children, and not to be out-done, his neighbour laughed and proclaimed that he had no less than fifteen. Ivor was duly impressed. "You are indeed well blessed," he said. "But don't you find it rather an expensive blessing? Fifteen birthday presents distributed through the year, and then at Christmas fifteen gifts all at the same time! How on earth do you manage?" "Oh, I do manage," said the old farmer, very slowly. "I do sell a cow!"

Date: 1973   *Source: John p 55*